WATER DIVINING
AND OTHER DOWSING

WATER DIVINING
AND OTHER DOWSING

A Practical Guide

Ralph Whitlock

David & Charles
Newton Abbot   London   North Pomfret (Vt)

British Library Catologuing in Publication Data

Whitlock, Ralph
  Water divining and other dowsing.
  1. Divining-rod
  I. Title
  183.3'23   BF1628

  ISBN 0-7153-8220-9

Typeset by Typesetters (Birmingham) Ltd.,
and printed in Great Britain
by A. Wheaton & Co., Exeter
for David & Charles (Publishers) Limited
Brunel House   Newton Abbot   Devon

Published in the United States of America
by David & Charles Inc
North Pomfret   Vermont 05053   USA

Contents

	Introduction	7
1	The Divining Rod	9
2	Discovering Water's Depth and Quantity	22
3	Dowsing for Other Substances	27
4	Dowsing for Objects	34
5	Dowsing and Plants	44
6	Dowsing and Insects	54
7	Dowsing, Health and Disease	59
8	Dowsing and the Fourth Dimension	73
9	Dowsing, Thought and Emotions	82
10	How Does Dowsing Work?	89
11	'Track Lines' and Megaliths	95
12	Dowsing from Maps and Photographs	103
13	The Road So Far	113
14	What Is It?	127
	Bibliography	137
	Index	141

Introduction

Writing about dowsing is a tricky exercise. I do not know what some of my readers, who have faithfully followed my incursions into the realms of folklore, natural history, prehistory and other facets of life in the countryside, will make of this book. Opinions about dowsing are as numerous as the persons who hold them.

I meet them all — the unprejudiced, the scornful, the doubters, the believers, the experts, the beginners.

Once when I dowsed for an underground passage on an archaeological 'dig' some of the professional archaeologists muttered darkly about it being a pity to introduce such mumbo-jumbo into a serious scientific project — and this despite the fact that my dowsing had been entirely successful and had saved a lot of exploratory digging. I was intrigued by the reaction of one of my granddaughters, then aged thirteen, when I showed her how to dowse and she felt the forked twig turning uncontrollably in her hands. Rejecting the evidence of her own senses, she exclaimed, 'I don't believe it!' On the other hand, an estate agent who called me in to check on the water resources of his land had such complete confidence in my ability to produce results that he expressed surprise at seeing me refer to my notes when estimating flow and depth. I gather that he expected me to know instinctively. And from time to time I attend meetings of dedicated dowsers for whom the contents of this book will correspond to a first school reader for a primary class. They are used to far more advanced stuff.

Some will reject what they read in these pages. Some will accept it so far and then halt, declaring they have reached the limits of their credibility. (It would be interesting to know how far they get before arriving at the sticking point.) Some will find the detailed instructions helpful. Some will be content to use the techniques for devising mystifying parlour tricks or for their own private treasure-hunting. And some will be inspired to employ those same techniques for more original research, of which plenty remains to be done. There is more scope for pioneering by the amateur in dowsing than in almost any other branch of the pursuit of knowledge.

The hero in H. G. Wells's story, *The Country of the Blind*, harassed by the hostility and disbelief of the blind community, came near to allowing himself to be deprived of his sense of sight in order to be like the rest of them. It would be an equal tragedy for a person who, had once discovered and experienced it, to be persuaded by ridicule and opposition to deny the existence of our still mysterious 'sixth sense'.

1

The Divining Rod

Mention dowsing and the conventional picture used to be of a horny-handed countryman, his set face distorted by grimaces, striding across a field clutching a forked twig in his outstretched hands. In a limited way the picture was accurate, but there is a growing awareness that the ability to dowse is by no means confined to horny-handed countrymen. Like so many old skills, crafts, cults and beliefs, dowsing has within the past twenty years enjoyed a resurgence of popularity. Its practitioners now range from housewives in suburban parlours to military personnel. (Certain Communist countries have corps of dowsers attached to their armies, and the United States Marines used dowsing extensively in the Vietnam war.)

My own experience, gained over some fifty years, suggests that at least 30 to 40 per cent of people, and probably more, possess the ability to dowse. Women and children seem more likely to be able to do so efficiently than labouring men with calloused hands.

When I give a demonstration of dowsing most of those present want to try their hand at it. Once when I was taking part in a BBC television programme, 'Pebble Mill at One', I found that neither the producer nor the presenter could get reaction from the divining rod, but several of the girl secretaries could. A gardener-groundsman produced a result that even I could not match − in a way which will be described later. We successfully located a bucket of water which had been buried under turf for our benefit, and we also discovered an underground water-pipe which no one knew about.

Perhaps the ability to dowse is like the ability to play a

musical instrument. Place four-part music sheets in front of me and I can hammer out simple tunes. My wife is much more accomplished but is also dependent on music sheets. Neither of us could hope to emulate, in a month of Sundays, those gifted musicians who can hear a tune once and then play it from memory, without ever seeing a printed score. Such musicians are born with the talent. Some of us can achieve a modest degree of proficiency by dogged practice. And some of us have no musical ability at all. It seems to be much the same with dowsing.

The conventional forked twig of the dowser is, in effect, simply the counterpart of the pointer on a spring-balance and has no intrinsic merit. The two arms of the fork are convenient because one can be held by each hand, but some dowsers operate efficiently with a straight wand. I am often asked, 'Is it necessary for the twig to be of hazel?' No, it is not. I have used elm, willow and a number of exotic woods overseas. The only criterion is that they must be reasonably fibrous and flexible and so able to stand stress without snapping. I doubt the statement that the ancient Druids used apple twigs; apple wood seems far too brittle. It is not even necessary to use wood at all. No doubt the convention arose centuries ago in rural areas where a twig cut from a hedge was the only tool readily available. Baling wire or wire from a coat-hanger is an acceptable substitute. I have often operated with a length of thickish wire, twisted to a convenient shape.

A typical dowsing rod is a forked twig of, say, ½in diameter at the tip of the pointer, tapering to ⅓ or ¼in at the end of the forks. Each arm of the fork is about a foot long. The base, or pointer, is perhaps 6—8in long. These are simply measurements of convenience. There is nothing sacrosanct about them.

Place your hands side by side, palms upwards, at waist level, chest level or somewhere in between. Place the forked twig on them, one of the arms on each palm. You will, of course, find that you have to hook your thumbs over the ends of the arms of the twig, to prevent it from tumbling to the ground. Now grasp the twig by closing your fingers over the arms. You will find a strong pressure developing on the angle between thumb and forefinger and on the outside of your little finger. Increase this pressure by forcing the arms of the twig apart, farther and

Correct way to hold a forked twig

farther. The reason for using a supple twig will now be evident;
a brittle twig will break or split under the strain. You will
probably find your arms drawn back until your hands have
moved back to touch your body. Keep up the extreme tension
but do not grasp the twig so tightly that it cannot move. The
pressure on your thumb and little finger should be intense, but
the pointer should be free to waggle up and down.

You are now ready to operate. Your arms, hands and the
forked twig have, in effect, become a piece of measuring
apparatus. They are in such tension that an extraneous force

can act upon them. The pointer is like the pointer on a spring balance, poised to register the strength of the force.

The traditional and most frequently employed purpose of dowsing is to locate underground springs and watercourses. Naturally the art is best practised out of doors. Go into a garden, field or park and, holding the twig as described, start to walk, slowly but at a steady pace. If underground water is present, as you approach it the twig will start to twist in your hands. If the spring is a strong one, the pointer will jerk up suddenly and hit you on the chest. Try to hold it down. Continue to grasp the ends of the fork as described and try to prevent the pointer from twisting upwards. You will not succeed. It may take the skin off your hands but it will still twist upwards.

You are now experiencing a natural force which has not yet been scientifically explained. In due course it probably will be, but at present we are in the dark as to what it is. Some dowsers explain that water gives off a 'ray' or current to which our bodies are susceptible. That may be so. All we can say, from our experience, is that there is some outside force manipulating that twig. We are certainly not doing it ourselves, either deliberately or subconsciously. Indeed, we have been experimenting in trying to prevent the twig from moving.

I have been asked whether the phenomenon has anything to do with an affinity between water and certain woods. The fact that I am able to use wire for the purpose effectively answers that question in the negative. Whatever the force may be, it is something which operates through the medium of the human body. As it still works when we are consciously trying to counteract it, it is evidently influencing the twig through some unexplored recesses of our brain. We are experiencing the workings of a mysterious 'sixth sense'.

Can the claim that what we are finding is evidence of underground water be substantiated? Of course. Admittedly it would not be feasible to sink a well or borehole in every instance, but where this has been done the success rate has been very high.

I learned the technique of water-divining from a colleague in the early 1930s. As a young reporter I was given the task of writing an article on dowsing. Two old countrymen who were reputed to be expert dowsers staged a demonstration for me. I was not a bit impressed and so wrote a highly critical article. A water engineer who was in charge of the appropriate department of a big agricultural trading and contracting firm then took me to task. He himself was an accomplished dowser. He selected sites by conventional methods for sinking new boreholes, but he also checked them with his divining twig. The two invariably tallied, as he was able to demonstrate when he sank the borehole. I spent a lot of time with him, learning how to use the twig for myself and becoming increasingly intrigued when the subsequent upsurge of water from deep in the earth proved that my reactions had been accurate.

Sometimes one encounters other types of confirmation of one's findings. Once in a drought-ridden region of northern Ghana I had circumstantial confirmation of a dowsing exercise I undertook. Having been persuaded to try to locate water in this village where it was badly needed I pinpointed a spot under a shady, spreading giant of a tree, the only tree of any size in the settlement. My pronouncement disappointed the villagers. 'Oh, we can't possibly dig there', they told me. 'It's a sacred tree!' The tree, like myself, had discovered a source of subterranean water. That is why it was flourishing so dramatically in that barren land, and that is why it was considered sacred.

Why was I so unimpressed by my very first encounter with dowsers? The explanation of what went wrong may prove of salutary value to anyone who wishes to become a proficient dowser.

We took those two old countrymen to a gently sloping meadow in Dorset and invited them to set to work. They worked across the slope, and wherever they claimed to locate water we stuck a marker in the ground. We were rather surprised by the number of underground streams they discovered — a dozen or more — but as this was well-watered country with a surface stream not far away, we accepted their findings as possible.

Then we took them to lunch at a pub some five or six miles

away and returned to the meadow by a circuitous route. Whether they recognised the meadow or not we did not know, but when we asked them to start operating again we did so on the other side of the field. Again we stuck in markers wherever they said they found water. And hardly any of this second set of markers agreed with those they had indicated before lunch! No wonder I concluded that dowsing was phony!

I feel sorry now for those two dowsers, who were countrymen of the old school, not very well educated but doing their best. They were not deliberately trying to bamboozle me. They were recording what they genuinely felt and could not imagine what had gone wrong.

'If you were to dig where we said you'd find water,' they kept asserting. 'But the places where you said it was before lunch are different from those you marked after lunch', we pointed out, and they had no answer to that. It made them unhappy, and I regret it now, for there *is* an answer.

Select a similar field, sloping towards a stream not too far away, so that the natural drainage and therefore the probable

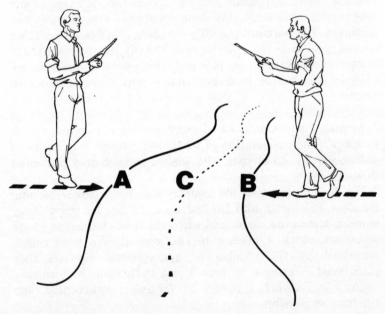

Determining the centre of an underground stream

14

direction of underground springs seems fairly obvious. (It is true that sometimes subterranean water does not follow surface indications, but it does often enough for this to be a reasonable test.) Walk across the slope, with the dowsing twig under tension. In due course, if springs are present, you will get a reaction. Immediately release the twig and mark the spot, walking on for 40 or 50yd. Turn round, face the marker you have placed and put the twig under tension again. Walk towards the marker again, and presently you will get the normal reaction, as you did before.

It will not, however, be at the marker but at a spot several yards before you reach it. What is happening is that you are getting your reaction before you are immediately over the spring. The underground water is midway between the two markers. My two old dowsers did not understand this, nor did I at the time, and hence we were all misled.

Stride 5 or 10yd down the slope and repeat the operation. You will now have two more markers, the centre of the subterranean spring lying midway between the two. Carry on repeating the exercise at intervals for the entire length of the field, and you will have two parallel lines of markers, often following a sinuous course. They provide visible evidence of the course of the underground water. The distance between the markers of each pair will depend on (a) the sensitivity of the dowser, (b) the size and strength of the stream and (c) the depth at which the water is to be found — any or all of these factors. The distance between the markers of each pair will, however, be constant.

The examples given so far have been simple, uncomplicated ones. In the instructions (above) for setting up markers, for instance, I have assumed that it is possible to detect the direction of the flow of the underground stream by surface indications, but that is not always so. Sometimes underground water flows at an angle to or even in the opposite direction to surface water. To a beginner such a discovery is usually intriguing.

To check the direction of flow of the water, stand in the middle of the stream zone you have marked out. Hold the twig in position and walk slowly along the centre of the band. If you are walking *against* the flow of the stream the pointer will lift; if you are walking *with* it, the pointer will dip.

It is not, incidentally, essential to work outdoors. I have often demonstrated the existence of underground springs beneath a lecture hall. On one such occasion recently, when I got a strong reaction alongside one wall of a room where I had been speaking, an elderly local resident exclaimed, 'Oh, you've found the course of the Ruttle Brook! It was built over years ago, but I can remember seeing it.'

I once had occasion to investigate an old house for prospective purchasers. Old residents in the neighbourhood asserted that the ground-floor rooms were subject to flooding and quoted alleged instances, but nothing of the sort had occurred within the past twenty or thirty years, and the estate agents and local council had no knowledge of it.

According to our informants, the flood water 'came from the rector's well', and we found that there *was* a disused well in the courtyard of the rectory next door. With my dowsing rod I traced a subterranean watercourse diagonally from the well, under the floors of the house and so to a roadside drain. We worked out that what had evidently happened many years earlier, perhaps a century or two, was that the rector's well had been apt to overflow in wet winters and to flood his own house. So a few feet below the top of the well he had had an overflow channel constructed, leading across what was then a plot of waste land to the roadside drain. Later someone built a house on that waste land. The flood occurred so infrequently that it was accepted as a natural hazard, but local tradition remembered the truth of the matter and the dowsing rod confirmed it. As it happened, two years later the house was flooded after a torrential thunderstorm.

A curious secondary feature of this investigation was that when tracing the line of the channel I got as strong a reaction from the rod when working in an upstairs room, three storeys up, as I did on the ground floor. Some dowsers have found that they can work perfectly well from horseback but that when they get a reaction from the rod the horse seems aware of it and becomes restive. Dowsing has also achieved results from a moving car and from an aeroplane; but more of these matters in a later chapter.

The forked twig has the advantages of being a convenient shape to hold and of being easily obtained, but, as already said, it is by no means the only sort of rod used by dowsers. The following are among the other devices employed:

1 A straight rod heavier at one end than at the other. Some dowsers prefer a hazel rod, newly cut from the 'stub' from which it has grown, which implies that it is a rod of about one year's growth. It is held by the thin end, usually by both hands, the thick end extending outwards at an angle from the body to a few inches above the surface of the ground. Over underground water the end of the rod begins to bob up and down. Because the rod is being held by its thin end it is, as with the forked twig, under considerable tension.

2 A straight rod, as described above but held in an arc; the user grasps its ends with both hands, held horizontally, palm downwards, at waist level. Considerable pressure is exerted to achieve a proper degree of tension.

3 A rod, either straight or forked, is balanced on the back of an outstretched hand.

4 A straight rod is cut into two pieces of equal length. The end of one is hollowed out a little, in order to make it slightly concave; an end of the other piece is pointed so that it will fit into the concavity. The other two ends are also carved slightly concave, so that the tip of a forefinger will easily fit into them. The two rods are fitted together and held at chest level by using the forefingers alone. The arms are outstretched as far as possible, thus increasing the tension. Alternatively, the two rods may be fitted together by means of forks at the end instead of concavities, if twigs with suitable forks can be found.

5 A forked rod may be made from any supple material. For example, dowsers of a generation or two ago, when whalebone corsets were fashionable, often operated with two whalebone strips, filched from their wives' foundation garments and tied together at one end. The free ends were held one in each hand exactly as with the arms of a forked hazel twig. Wire of any metal or even plastic may be twisted into the correct shape and should prove quite satisfactory.

6 Wire, being flexible, can be twisted into any shape, and one

favoured by some dowsers is a semi-circle with a straightened hand-grip at either end. There are several ways of holding this apparatus. One is with palms upwards, as I hold a forked twig; another is with palms downwards, with the thumb taking much of the pressure; a third, using thin wire, is to hold it delicately between thumb and finger (the third finger of each hand, say some).

7 Some dowsers operate with big circular rods held with hands palm downwards. The circle is not quite complete, and one hand grasps either end of the rod. Aluminium wire has been used successfully.

8 To make an angle-rod from wire, bend a length of wire at right-angles so that one arm is approximately four times as long as the other. The short arm is the handle. Hold it with an extended arm, the long arm pointing forward. As subterranean water is approached, the long arm will swing back towards the body. Dowsers often use two angle-rods, one in each hand. These will react by swinging in and crossing each other when locating water. (*Note.* Although many dowsers get excellent results from indicators made of wire, the use of metal can sometimes create confusion, in that the metal may be reacting to substances other than water.)

9 Some gifted dowsers can work without any mechanical aids at all. They will hold their clasped hands extended in front of them and will get the same reaction as if they were holding a twig or rod. I can sometimes get a slight reaction by this method but not nearly as strong as with a rod. I feel a slight tingling in my hands, which tend to lift automatically. Other dowsers have told me they feel a tingling in their feet.

In the early 1960s a young South African boy achieved fame by being able to detect underground water without any aids. He said that he saw the water 'shimmering like green moonlight' in the ground.

There are limitations to the type of water supply that can be detected by the dowsing rod. The rod does not react to open water, except that some dowsers do get a reaction as they approach the banks of a swiftly-flowing river (though not over the river itself).

My experience at Pebble Mill was unusual in that I (and the gardener-groundsman) managed to find a bucket of water hidden under the turf. To detect still water in a small bucket needs a fair measure of ability or plenty of practice, though it is true that the bucket was only a few inches beneath the surface. The discovery of the unrecorded waterpipe was the sort of result more to be expected.

The incident produced another unusual feature. As already described, when the dowser passes over subterranean water the pointer of his twig springs up and smacks him on the chest. That is the normal reaction with most dowsers, though with some the reaction is reversed: the twig dips. Some experts explain that when a dowser in whose hands the twig normally twists upwards experiences a downward dip, the water he has located will be polluted. In detecting this concealed bucket I obtained the usual upward movement of the pointer, but with the gardener-groundsman the pointer jerked downwards. When we dug up the bucket we found that the water was indeed polluted, by soil which had fallen in when it had been buried.

The Pendulum

An acceptable alternative to the divining rod is the pendulum. In some respects it is indeed easier to use, and it is considerably more versatile. As a rule, most dowsers reserve divining rods for outdoor work and particularly for the location of underground water. The pendulum is more suited to investigations indoors, where it is protected from the wind, and to the delicate work of map dowsing, medical dowsing and other operations to be described in later chapters.

Any heavy object suspended on a length of string or thread will serve as a pendulum. Practical considerations impose limits on its weight for the purpose of dowsing, for it has to be held between thumb and one finger, sometimes for longish periods. Also it is better to avoid a bob made of metal, or you may find yourself locating metal of the same sort as the bob instead of the water or whatever you are searching for.

I myself use a cylinder of wood cut from a growing tree. It is about ¾in in diameter and 2in long and is suspended by a

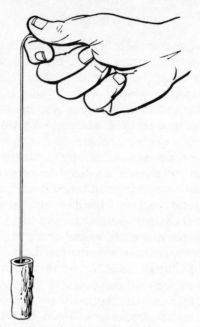

Holding a pendulum, skewer hidden in the hand

thread inserted through it lengthwise. The other end of the thread is wound around a wooden rod about the size of a pencil — it is, in fact, a meat skewer.

A complication arises from the fact that the reaction of the pendulum varies from person to person. A good way of achieving a proper co-operation between yourself and your pendulum is to test the pendulum over a known stream, probably one you have located by means of a divining rod. Standing over the centre of this subterranean watercourse extend the arm and hold the thread of the pendulum between thumb and one finger. Very soon the pendulum will begin either to oscillate or gyrate. The motion I experience is oscillation. Establish what the reaction is for you, and then you can dowse over unknown territory. The pattern will be consistent.

A word of warning. The pendulum's cord length may create some confusion. What I have described here is the normal reaction with a short pendulum (ie a pendulum with a short cord, of a few inches in length). Chapter 3 reveals that various substances react to cords of various lengths. Thus, water gives a reaction to a cord length of 26½in. When I test an underground source with a pendulum with a cord of that length the oscillatory movement changes to gyration. But more of that later.

Once you have established the type of reaction that is normal for you, proceed as with a divining rod. It is possible, however, to take a short cut. Supposing you are confronted by a large field or wide expanse of open country to investigate, which promises to take you all day. Choose a base line, which may well be the edge of the field, and face the territory to be surveyed. Extend your left hand at shoulder level, fingers together, thumb uppermost, as a pointer. In your right hand, held at the same level but approximately at right angles to the left arm, hold the thread of the pendulum between thumb and one finger, using the length of thread which you have established as correct for underground water. Turn your body very gradually, so that by degrees a projection of the line of your left arm would cover the entire expanse of country. At first the pendulum will be oscillating gently, but when your left hand is pointing in the direction of an underground spring the oscillations will change to gyrations (or vice versa, if you are that sort of dowser). Now move, say, 20yd along your base line and repeat the exercise. The point in the field at which the two lines you have discovered intersect is where you will go to start a more detailed search for water, by methods already described.

My experience for that television programme at Pebble Mill has shown how polluted water may be indicated by a reaction of the divining rod opposite to that for pure water. An underground source may also be tested by the pendulum. Having established that water is present, stand over the centre of the stream and allow the pendulum to work up a good gyration (if that is what the pendulum does with you). Then place your upturned left hand under it. If the gyrations increase in strength, the water is pure; if they cease or change from gyrations to oscillations, or if they start to gyrate in the opposite direction (anticlockwise if hitherto they have been clockwise), the water is polluted.

2

Discovering Water's Depth and Quantity

Having established the presence of water beneath the surface, it is useful, indeed often essential, to determine the depth at which it occurs and whether the quantity available is sufficient to justify sinking a well or borehole.

When I first started dowsing this seemed to me a virtually impossible exercise. As described in Chapter 1, I demonstrated the course of the underground stream by a series of parallel markers. It seemed logical to assume that if the parallels were far apart the stream was a strong one, for I was picking up its influence at some distance from its centre. Or was it simply because the water was near the surface? The strength of the rod's reaction to the stream could depend on two factors, depth and quantity, and I found it impossible to separate them.

Then an experienced dowser showed me how to proceed. I had to stand with my rod at the ready in the centre of the stream band and walk away at a right angle from its course. At a certain point (not necessarily the same point that I marked when approaching the stream from the opposite direction) the rod would lift. The distance between this point and my starting point would represent approximately the depth at which the water would be found. When working on clay, which is a troublesome substance, allow 10—20 per cent extra.

From this second point I continued to walk in the same direction and presently found the rod lifting again. I marked this third point. My mentor told me that the distance, in average paces, between the second and third points, multiplied

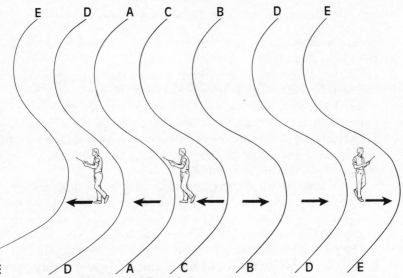

Determining the depth and flow of water

by ten, was approximately equal to the flow of water in the underground stream, measured in gallons per hour! And so it was for him, but not for me. We were able to check our accuracy here, for the stream was subsequently tapped not far from where we had been experimenting. To obtain the correct answer, which tallied with that of my colleague, I had to multiply by 30. I cannot offer a complete explanation, for I cannot explain why the method should work at all, but it seems that I was perhaps more sensitive than my colleague. This particular stream was yielding about 210gal/hr. I walked seven paces between points 2 and 3, whereas my fellow dowser had to walk 21 paces.

Another method of determining quantity that is used by some dowsers is to place a marker above the centre of an underground stream band and walk in circles round it. The dowser must first test his reactions by operating over a known watercourse with a known flow. Walking around his marker in a circle with a radius of, say, 5 or 6ft he has to record the number of times he completes the circle before his rod, under tension, starts to lift. He then divides the known flow of water (so many gallons per hour) by the number of completed circles, arriving at the equation that one circle=x gallons per hour. If possible, repeat the exercise on more sites, to check the accuracy of your findings. The formula, once established, will then hold good for new sources.

I have, however, come across a practical snag over this method. Not long ago I determined to try it again, in a place where I knew I would have the opportunity of testing it again over a known watercourse before venturing on the unknown. Unfortunately I found myself operating on such a rocky and muddy site that holding the rod at tension for even one complete circle was impossible.

When dowsing for depth and/or quantity, some dowsers use a horseshoe magnet pressed against the rod, which they say accentuates the reaction. The magnet is held in one hand alongside the rod, with the rounded end towards the pointer.

The pendulum may also be used for determining depth, and here, not for the first or last time in the study of dowsing, we encounter a phenomenon which would be incredible if it had not been shown, many a time, to produce results.

Stand at a point which has been established as over the centre of the subterranean stream. Hold the pendulum between thumb and one finger of the outstretched arm. Soon the pendulum will start to oscillate, which is the signal to start counting, at a steady rate and *aloud*. Presently the oscillations will, quite suddenly, switch to gyrations. Make a note of the number reached in the counting when that happens.

Some dowsers claim that the number represents the depth in feet at which the water will be found. That may well be true for them (for, as with everything else in dowsing, there is much variation, depending on the individual), but as a general rule it seems too facile. I recommend that the beginner experiments with a few known streams already tapped by boreholes, so that he can check his findings against established facts. Thus he will be able to determine his own scale.

A similar counting method can be used with the forked twig. Stand at the centre of the stream band and grasp the arms of the twig in the approved manner. When the pointer jerks upwards, which will happen almost immediately, release one arm of the fork. Then grasp it again and start counting. When the pointer lifts again, the number reached will be the same as that discovered by the pendulum, and it will indicate the depth below the surface at which the water exists. Whether the number refers to feet, yards, metres or whatever depends on the scale established by the dowser concerned, as described in the previous paragraph.

In yet another technique a straight hazel wand is employed. Hold it by the thin end, as described on page 00, with the rod extended at an angle from the body and the thick end a few inches above the surface of the ground. The stance is much the same as that of a golfer, holding his putter at the ready as he contemplates the next stroke, or that of a treasure-hunter exploring the ground with a detector. Soon the thick end will start to jig up and down, and the moment this happens the dowser starts to count. He continues until the rod changes its motion from bobbing up and down to swinging backwards and forwards. At that point he ceases counting, and the number reached bears a relationship to the depth at which water will be found. Some dowsers multiply the number by 10, which they claim give the depth in feet. It is up to every dowser to determine his own scale by testing against known data.

Reverting to the forked twig, it is possible to get some indication of depth by changing the level at which the twig is held. Hold the hands, grasping the twig at tension, as far aloft as possible and gradually lower them. Note the distance above ground reached when the normal dowsing reaction occurs. With this technique, too, some dowsers say that the height above ground, measured in feet and multiplied by 10, will give the depth in feet. In any case, the result should correspond precisely with those obtained by the other methods described.

So far it has been assumed that the underground water searched for exists in streams or veins in the rocks, but water also occurs in underground lakes or pools.

The presence of such a natural subterranean reservoir is indicated by the unusual behaviour of the rod. After lifting, the pointer, instead of dropping back to the inert position after a few paces, continues to press upwards against one's chest. Go back to the starting point, move a few yards to the right or left and repeat the operation. By a series of such exercises one boundary of the underground lake can soon be established, but how far does it extend in the other direction? This can be determined by walking straight across it.

Starting at the point where the rod first reacted, walk forward a few paces, until the rod lifts again. Stop and take one hand away from the rod, to break the continuity of the reaction. Then put the twig under tension again and resume walking. This time you will go twice the number of paces before the rod lifts. Repeat the process. As you advance you will find that the number of paces between each lift of the pointer increases in a roughly arithmetical progression, eg three, six, nine, twelve, and so on. When, after a time, the number of paces between each reaction starts to decrease, it means that you have passed the centre of the underground pool and are moving towards the far side of the perimeter.

Underground sheets of water discovered by this method may prove to be artesian. A recent American theory states that in certain geological structures 'domes' of water exist, fed from sources deep in the earth. A dowser who discovers one of these 'domes' should be cautious about recommending anyone to tap it. Better to explore the perimeter first and find out how many streams are emanating from it and whether they are already being tapped. Otherwise the man who sinks a bore into a dome may find he has obtained an abundant supply of water but his neighbours' supplies have dried up.

Recently on a rural estate I found that a series of springs were emerging from a hillside on the same contour. The hill above was far too big to check for a 'dome' of water by dowsing across it, but I did follow the critical contour for about a mile and discovered a dozen or so springs. I surmised that here rain falling on the hill seeped into the soil but at the contour in question encountered a stratum of impervious rock. Fortunately the estate owner preferred to have a number of small sources of water at frequent intervals rather than one large source high on the hill and so was well satisfied.

Many dowsers get no reaction to sheets of underground water, for the reason that they react only to moving water. Lyall Watson, in his book *Supernature*, states that 'Water, by the action of friction between itself and the soil, creates a field that could have electro-magnetic qualities'. This he includes among the few bits of 'hard knowledge about dowsing' that we possess. But an underground lake or a rock stratum saturated with water produces no friction. Or does it?

3
Dowsing for Other Substances

This book has so far confined itself to dowsing for water, but the art of dowsing is subject to no such limitations. The rod and/or pendulum can indicate the presence of almost any substance. Possible explanations of the phenomena are discussed in later chapters; for the present we will restrict ourselves to practical matters.

Doubtless many dowsers have become preoccupied with divining for water because (a) water, a basic human need, is frequently in short supply and (b) subterranean sources of water produce a ready reaction from the forked twig and other dowsing devices. It is noteworthy that many of the instances quoted by writers on dowsing refer to India, parts of Africa, the western states of America and Canada and similar arid regions where water is at a premium. However, discovering sources of water is by no means the only purpose for which dowsing has been traditionally employed. From early times it has been used to detect the presence of minerals and metal ores.

A classic publication on the subject of dowsing for minerals is the sixteenth-century book *De Re Metallica*, written by one Georgius Agricola (which is a latinised form of the German name, Georg Bauer, or George the Peasant). Agricola was in the 1520s the resident doctor at a mining camp in Joachimsthal, in the Erzegebirge Mountains of southern Germany and northern Bohemia (that same valley from which the word 'dollar' is derived). Fascinated by the turbulent activities of this boom town, where new veins of silver were still being discovered, he set about making himself conversant with every aspect of mining lore. The resultant book is encyclopedic and served as a mining textbook for a century or two after publication.

In some of the carefully executed woodcuts, stated to have been prepared at great expense, with which the book is illustrated dowsers are depicted searching with forked twigs for new veins of ore. Their methods are described in the text. A forked twig of hazel wood was evidently the favourite device in Agricola's day, but he says that some dowsers used a different wood for each metal. Hazel was regarded as having a special affinity for silver. Rods of iron were also said to be employed for locating gold and silver, though one would imagine that the rods would have to be pliable, like wire.

Although Agricola's book gives the use of dowsing rods by miners a respectable antiquity, the practice is much older than the sixteenth century. When in 1936 a coin was struck to commemorate the millennium of the discovery of a famous silver mine in Rammelsberg, a mountain near Goslar, Germany, the design included the figure of a dowser, thus testifying to a belief or tradition that the mine had been found by means of the dowsing rod. Dowsing for ores is said to have been known, too, in ancient Scythia and China.

The information that dowsing can be used to find a multitude of substances naturally suggests complications. How can the dowser know what substance is influencing his rod or pendulum? A direct method involves the use of samples and can be employed with either divining rod or pendulum. A sample of the substance which is to be the object of the search is held in one hand against the rod or against the thread of the pendulum. The rod or pendulum then reacts only to that material.

Doubt has been expressed as to whether the sample does anything more than help to focus the dowser's mind. It seems that if he concentrates on locating, for instance, a lode of silver, silver is what he will find (that is, of course, if there is any present). Once when I was searching for a lost tunnel on an archaeological site, I found it through the normal reaction of my forked twig, without using a sample. (It is said that to dowse for 'space', which is how a tunnel could be described, the sample held against the rod or pendulum should be an empty

28

bottle or some other empty container.) I proceeded exactly as I would have done if dowsing for water, but instead of discovering an underground stream I located the underground passage on which I was concentrating.

An alternative method that can be employed with the pendulum has already been referred to. With the long pendulum the length of the cord indicates the substance discovered. It is up to every dowser to establish his own scale of lengths, for in this as in nearly every other aspect of dowsing, performance varies a little with the individual. Test the pendulum first against samples of any substances you want to find and compile a table of data which are true for you. Once you have established the length of cord from which you get a response for a particular material, you can be assured that for the future that is the length of cord which will give you a reaction for that substance.

The following table gives the approximate cord-lengths for certain common substances. Though small variations will occur with some dowsers, the order in which the substances are placed is probably true for everyone.

Substance	Cord length (inches)
Sulphur	7
Carbon	12
Concrete	13
Silicon, glass, etc.	14
Silver and lead	22
Diamond	24
Aluminium	25
Water	26½
Gold	29
Copper	30½
Iron	32

It is curious that the length of cord for diamonds is exactly double that for carbon, of which, of course, diamonds are a form. This is probably more than coincidence, but its significance is uncertain. Incidentally, the length for oxygen is the same as that for water, so a rusty nail (the rust being iron oxide) will give reactions of 32in for iron and 26½in for oxygen.

Dowsing over an area of ground which contains nothing of particular interest can produce a response when the cord length is 20in, this being the cord length for organic matter. The pendulum may be reacting to vegetation or to the worms beneath it. Hold it over a loaf of bread or a dish of cabbage or your own foot and you will get the same reaction.

Yet another method for determining the substance discovered can be used with both rod or pendulum. Here again a good deal of preparation is necessary, for before any original work is attempted you need to prepare a table showing the standard reaction of the rod or pendulum to a range of substances *when the dowsing device is being used by you*. It can be a useful occupation for winter evenings.

For this operation use a *short* pendulum, with a cord not longer than about 8in (preferably rather shorter) and keep it at the same length throughout the test. Put a sample on a table before you and hold the pendulum over it (holding the cord between thumb and one finger as in previous exercises). After a time it will start to gyrate. Stop the motion by clasping your hands together; then resume the former position and allow the pendulum to start gyrating again. After being interrupted in this way for a few times the pendulum will sulk and refuse to gyrate any more. The number of times it will resume its gyrations before finally going on strike is constant for the subject under test.

Thus, when testing over water most dowsers find that the pendulum will start its gyrations only twice before going dead. The number thus obtained is known as that substance's *Serial Number*; so the Serial Number for water is 2. The Serial Number for iron is 4, for silver 6 or 7, for gold 11. Here again, though, small variations are experienced by individual dowsers, so it is as well for each person to prepare his own table. Once established, for him the Serial Numbers will not vary.

With certain substances, usually complex ones, a complicated reaction may be experienced. Supposing that the normal behaviour of a pendulum in your hand is an anti-clockwise gyration, you may find that after a few interruptions the pendulum starts to move clockwise. Do not be discouraged; keep going. You will find that eventually the clockwise gyrations also cease, leaving you with, say, four anti-clockwise gyrations and three clockwise. The formula may be expressed by the use of a minus sign; 4−3. And that, for you, will be the reaction you will always obtain from the short pendulum over that particular substance.

Precisely the same technique may be employed with the divining rod or forked twig. Hold the twig under tension over the sample. When the pointer lifts, halt and release one arm. Grasp it again, put under tension, and the reaction will be resumed. Repeat the sequence until you get no further reaction. The number of times the rod has lifted is the Serial Number for that substance, and it will correspond with the Serial Number determined by using the pendulum.

Dowsing by Colours

Dowsing by colours is an intriguing byway which may perhaps take us very little farther in our investigations but is nevertheless worth exploring. Its possibilities were apparently discovered by the French Professor Henri Mager in the early years of the present century and described in his book *Water Diviners and their Methods.*

After many experiments he prepared a device now known as *Mager's Rosette.* It consists of a circle divided into eight equal segments, each of a different colour. The circle is arranged with

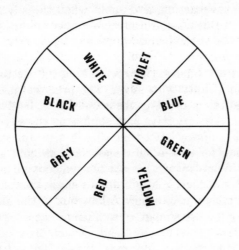

Mager's Rosette

the violet segment at the top, and if the Rosette is placed on a flat surface this segment should coincide with the North, as on a map. The other colours are arranged as follows, reading clockwise from the violet: blue, green, yellow, red, grey, black, white.

For use with a dowsing rod or forked twig the Mager Rosette has to be of respectable dimensions, say, 2 or 3ft in diameter, or even more. You have to place it on the ground and walk around it, taking care to avoid the vicinity of underground streams. As you slowly pace the circle you will find the pointer lifting at each of the four cardinal points — north, east, south and west, or, on your colour chart, violet, green, red and black.

Dowsing by colours is based on the existence of affinities between certain colours and certain substances, though not necessarily the colours which those substances themselves possess. To determine an affinity, take a sample of a substance and place it at random on any one of the coloured segments. Let us experiment with silver, taking care to use pure silver and not the debased modern currency which is not silver at all.

We will suppose that we have placed our piece of silver on the yellow sector. If we now pace around the Rosette with the rod under tension we shall get no reaction at all. Move the silver to the red segment and repeat the perambulation. Again there will be no reaction, and again when the silver is on the grey segment. But when the silver is moved to the black sector the pointer lifts at the four cardinal points, exactly as when no sample was present.

So we have established that on the Mager Rosette the colour black has an affinity with silver. The practical use of this is that when dowsing for silver the colour black, held against the dowsing rod, is as effective as a sample as the silver itself. It can be readily appreciated that this is a useful substitution when dowsing for a rare substance such as gold. Carrying a gold object in one's pocket is not always convenient.

As a matter of fact, gold provides a slight complication, for it has an affinity not to a pure colour but to the line between green and yellow. A similar phenomenon occurs with certain other substances, such as lead, which has an affinity somewhere between red and grey. It is possible by trial and error to determine the exact shade of colour to which one of these 'difficult' substances has an affinity, establishing, for instance, whether the affinitive colour for gold is nearer yellow than green or just what mixture of the two gives the strongest reaction.

These phenomena can, of course, be studied just as well by means of a pendulum as by a forked twig; perhaps more easily, for then one can use a smaller Rosette. Some dowsers take the trouble to paint their rods or pendulums the colour which has an affinity for the substance they are seeking. Thus copper, which has an affinity for dark violet, can be located by using a rod or pendulum painted dark violet.

W. H. Trinder, in his book *Dowsing*, describes how he tests a known underground stream for purity of water by employing a method based on colour affinities. For water the affinitive colour is violet. He prepares a series of rods or samples painted with shades of violet, from very pale to deep violet-blue. Starting with the palest he paces, with this rod in his hand, across a stream zone. If the rod lifts in the normal way, the water is drinkable. But if he gets no reaction or only a light one till he reaches the deep violet and then finds the rod jerking sharply, the water is polluted.

As a further exercise, by following the course of a polluted underground stream with the deep violet-blue rod or colour sample in the hand, it is sometimes possible to trace the source of pollution, perhaps a silage pit or some factory effluent. In rural districts in former times the effluent from farm dung-heaps was commonly allowed to seep into the soil (it still does, in some instances), and I have on several occasions traced the course of the effluent underground. If there are no obstructions the reactions of the rod to deep violet-blue become fainter and fainter, and one can run through the gamut of shades of violet until the palest is reached. This sequence is particularly noticeable in chalk country, chalk being a well-known purifying agent. Old Wiltshire countrymen used to say that polluted water had only to flow over nine stones (flint) or nine lumps of chalk to become purified.

4

Dowsing for Objects

Our study of dowsing, which began simply with an investigation of the reactions of a forked twig to underground water, has now greatly widened its scope. We have seen that we have at our disposal several dowsing devices of considerable versatility. They are the forked twig, the straight rod, sundry devices made of wire twisted or bent into different shapes, the short pendulum and the long pendulum. With their aid we have learned how to 'find' not only water but a wide range of substances, mostly metals or minerals. We have also learned how to identify the substances we locate by means of serial numbers and colour affinities, and we have seen how these numbers and colours may be used as alternatives to the actual substances when we wish to use a sample in our work.

Now let us consider what practical use we can make of all this information.

Dowsing for water can be fun, especially if we have an uninitiated audience! Readers who happen to live in an arid, drought-stricken part of the world may well find the ability to dowse a valuable asset, but those of us whose home is in a country with an adequate rainfall and the amenity of a piped water supply will have little chance of putting it to practical use. From time to time I am asked to advise on the best place for a new borehole, but the requests are not very frequent. The time when my services were most in demand for water divining was during Britain's abnormally dry summers in 1976 and 1977, when householders wanted to know the location of forgotten wells. More frequently I am called in to locate forgotten drains and water-pipes.

Nor is it likely that we shall have much opportunity to dowse for a new lode of silver or gold (though most dowsers have occasional dreams of discovering an oil well!). For the most part our dowsing will be concerned with objects. We shall exercise our skill in treasure-hunting — whether for items of archaeological or monetary value is immaterial. To do so is quite feasible. I cannot think of anything that a metal detector can do which is outside the capacity of a dowsing device in the hands of an efficient dowser.

For a start, let us dowse for a coin buried in the garden. We can use any of the dowsing devices described. If we decide on the forked twig, the straight rod or the short pendulum we can employ either a sample (actual or colour affinity) or the appropriate serial number. If we are going to use the long pendulum we adjust the cord to the right length for the substance we hope to find. For a nickel coin (modern coinage) the correct length for the cord will be 32½in, for a copper coin 30½in. (These are average lengths; every dowser must check to determine whether they are true for him.)

Let us suppose that the coin is a copper one, obligingly buried in the garden for us, in our absence. We take up position at one side of the garden plot and stand with the cord of the pendulum held between thumb and one finger of the right hand, at 30½in above the bob. Set the pendulum swinging. Stretch out the left arm at an angle of 45° to the body and point to the ground. Move this arm slowly backwards and forwards, sweeping the surface of the garden.

At a certain point the pendulum will cease oscillating and begin a circular movement. Place a marker in the ground at the point to which you were pointing when this happened. Go to a side of the garden at right angles to the one where you have been standing and repeat the exercise. When the pendulum starts to gyrate, stick in another marker.

From the point where you were first standing, project a line through the first marker. From the point where you were standing when you made the second observation, project a line through the second marker. The point at which the two lines intersect is very near the buried coin. To improve on the accuracy, approach the point of intersection with the pendulum oscillating. When the pendulum switches from oscillation to gyration, which will be at a short distance from the point, insert a marker in the ground. Approach the point of intersection from another direction, and again you will get a reaction before you reach it. Insert another marker. Keep repeating the operation and you will soon have a circle of markers. The copper coin will be under the precise centre of the circle.

As already intimated, you can follow the same procedure using a forked twig, a short pendulum or any other dowsing device. Having acquired a certain degree of confidence by successfully locating buried coins, we may well choose to turn our attention now to unknown territory. The garden will do. We do not know what is beneath the soil, but we can find out. Using the same long pendulum we can begin a process of analysis.

If the pendulum switches from oscillation to gyration when the cord is 12in long there is carbon beneath the surface of the soil, perhaps the remains of a bag of soot. Lengthen the cord to 13in and we shall discover any lumps of concrete, broken slates and similar debris that may be lying around. A cord 14in long will reveal any buried glass; 15in leads us to glazed pottery, such as the shards of a broken saucer; 22in to silver or lead; 25in to broken flower-pots and unglazed earthenware and also any aluminium that has somehow found its way into the garden; 29in to gold (if we should be so lucky!); 30½in to copper; 32in to iron; 32½in to nickel, which probably indicates a 10p piece which someone has lost.

Before sitting down to write these paragraphs I made just such an exploration in my garden. Having marked out a square yard I went over it slowly and methodically with a long pendulum and noted the cord lengths at which I obtained reactions. Then I dug over the plot to a depth of about 12in and sifted the soil through a sieve. I found soot (12in for carbon), broken glass (14in) and a broken tea-cup (15in). Reaction to the 20-in cord length indicated organic matter or vegetation (though it *can* mean electricity) and was probably due to weeds, though maybe to a worm or two. Some shards of an old flower-pot produced a reaction on the 25-in cord length. Water is indicated by a cord length of 26½in and, not surprisingly, was present. The iron implied by a reaction on a cord length of

32in proved to be a couple of old nails. Nothing at all unusual or exciting, but the findings of the pendulum were vindicated at every point.

In certain other experiments I have made the results have not been so complete. In one I failed at first to find the earthernware indicated. Then I dug the ground again to a depth of 2ft instead of 1, and found some bits of pottery. So perhaps any failures were due to my not digging deep enough.

The technique is so reliable and provides such comprehensive results that one wonders why it is not more extensively used in archaeological 'digs'. Employed over a pristine site before digging begins it can indicate the most fruitful areas for research, and archaeologists can be forewarned about what they may expect to find.

Analysis of a site can be conducted by means of a rod or a short pendulum just as easily as by a long pendulum. It must be rememberd, however, that with those two methods we are using a different scale. The Serial Numbers for substances in no way correspond to the lengths of cord required for the long pendulum to locate them. The Serial Number for iron, for instance, is 4, not 32; for copper 5, not 30½; for silver 7, not 22.

With both scales every dowser should check his own reactions for each substance before he can hope to achieve accurate results. He may find that the numbers he obtains differ slightly from those given.

Colour affinities, however, do not appear to depend on the individual dowser. They are constant.

Some Complications, Snags and Problems

Dowsing abounds with snags and problems. Nothing in nature is simple. As the basis of the art of science of dowsing is so far unexplained, it is no wonder that some of the complications and apparent anomalies seem inexplicable.

One complication, however, is easily explained and dealt with. I have sometimes been asked how, when analysing a plot of ground, or indeed anything else, dowsing will identify composite substances. The answer is that the pendulum (or other dowsing device) reacts to the separate elements that make up the compound. For instance, if the soil has been recently dressed with sulphate of ammonia you might expect to get reactions for sulphur (a cord of 7in), nitrogen (20in) and oxygen (26½in). A rusty nail or horse-shoe will give reactions to cord lengths of both 32in (iron) and 26½in (oxygen), thus indicating iron oxide.

Another problem which can cause momentary puzzlement, but which can be easily explained, sometimes arises when only one of the substances for which you have obtained reactions can be found. A copper coin has been buried for you to find. In due course you discover it by using a cord length of 30½in. But wait, there is something else: the pendulum is also reacting with a cord length of 25in. Nothing else is visible in the soil. The solution is to dig deeper: down there you will probably find a deposit of smashed earthenware to which the pendulum has shown itself sensitive.

Less easy to resolve are the problems arising from the fact that the length of cord in the long pendulum is the same for several unrelated substances. Thus 22in is the length of cord for not only silver but also lead and salt. Not only most organic substances but also electricity react to 20in, and water and oxygen to 26½in. A pendulum reacting to a substance when operating with a 29in cord may excite the dowser with the anticipation of finding gold, but his discovery may be only a stone rich in silicon. It is interesting that iron pyrites, the mineral popularly known as 'false gold' because of its propensity to deceive the novice by its visual similarity to gold, deceives the pendulum as well.

We now have to encounter the problem of interruption or interference. As a demonstration of how this operates, take a long pendulum and set it to work over, say, a lump of iron, for which the cord length has to be 32in. In your other hand hold a piece of chalk. When the pendulum is nicely gyrating, transfer your chalk to the hand holding the pendulum. The gyration will immediately cease, and after a short break the pendulum will start to oscillate. Transfer the chalk back to your left hand, and the pendulum will resume its gyrations.

Certain substances, of which calcium is one, have the property of interfering with the pendulum or dowsing rod. Chalk is, of course, calcium carbonate, hence its efficacy in the example given above. Other such substances include potassium, aluminium, magnesium, sodium and lead, all of them either as pure elements or in compounds. T. C. Lethbridge, author of several books on dowsing and related subjects, calls these substances 'interruptors'. In practice, interruptors, when present, interfere very effectively with a dowser's activities. By imposing a kind of block, they can prevent him from locating an object known to be in the vicinity. The remedy is to track down the interruptors, by any of the methods used for determining their presence, and if possible remove them.

Thus, supposing we are tracing the course of a subterranean iron pipe by using a pendulum with a cord 32in long. Suddenly we arrive at a point where the pendulum goes dead. Have we arrived at the end of the pipe, or is something interfering with the pendulum? We examine with the pendulum a point several feet farther on, where the pipe should be if it is following a straight line. If we find there the normal reaction for iron, we can assume that the break was due to interference, not to the absence of the pipe. So now we investigate the gap to determine what substance is providing the interference. Trying various cord lengths we get a reaction when the length is 22in. That is the length for calcium, sodium and lead (as well as silver). Digging down, we look for traces of any of these substances. Sodium is unlikely, but we may find a scrap of old window lead or, what is more probable, some chalk. Remove it and try the pendulum again, with a cord length of 32in. We should now be able to trace the missing section of the pipe without difficulty. (However, it is as well to wait for a few hours, perhaps a day or so, as the influence of the chalk or whatever it is will take time to disperse.)

Many British dowsers in the early and middle years of the present century were Army officers who practised much of their dowsing in India. There they became familiar with the frustrating phenomenon of the Deccan Trap. I too have dowsed for water in the Deccan and have seen my predictions proved wrong. The Deccan Trap is a stratum of slightly radioactive volcanic rock which, it seems, acts not exactly as an interruptor but a disturbing influence, throwing normal dowsing reactions out of focus.

Cones and Auras

On page 16 I relate how, when dowsing for a forgotten water-channel under an old house in a Somerset village, my forked twig gave as strong a reaction when I was testing in an upstairs room as when I was working at ground level. The influence (however one can define it) of the channel extended some distance upwards. That, of course, is what we would expect from the evidence that dowsing can be practised on horseback and from the experiences of Russian scientists who have found that they can operate from an aeroplane flying at considerable heights.

T. C. Lethbridge, in *ESP: Beyond Time and Distance* (published in 1965), describes a discovery which takes our knowledge of this phenomenon a stage farther. Placing an object on the floor of a room he approached it with a pendulum, which reacted a short distance before he reached it. Approaching it from various angles and marking the points at which the pendulum reacted he found, as was to be expected, that the points formed a circle around the object. The radius of the circle was precisely the same as the cord length of the pendulum required to locate the object. Thus, as a glass marble would need a cord length of 14in, so the radius of the circle would also be 14in. For an iron object, the two measurements would be 32in.

Leaving the object where it was, he went upstairs, took up a position immediately above it and repeated the experiment. Again the points he marked formed a circle, but it was a smaller circle than the one downstairs. The object with which he was working happened to be of copper, which reacts to a cord length of 30½in, so his marks formed a circle of 30½in radius. At the level of the upper floor, 9ft above the floor on which the copper object was still resting, the radius of the circle was only 23in.

The implication is that the object was surrounded by a field of force which extended, in a form which could be detected by the pendulum, at a distance of 30½in when measured on the same plane. This field of force also extended upwards (and, as was shown later, downwards as well) but contracted at the rate of 7½in in 108in. In short, the field of force was double cone-shaped, one cone extending upwards and the other downwards, from the place on which the object was resting.

Lethbridge said, however, that he had not managed to find the tip of a cone. The cones seem to taper away to infinity. He wondered what the world would look like if we could see them, as we can see light waves. Certainly it would appear very different from the world at present visible to our limited senses.

This looks like confirmatory evidence of another phenomenon which has long been reputed to exist, the aura. The haloes which surround the heads of holy men in paintings are said by some to be attempts by the artists to depict an aura of light emanating from these people. During recent decades the existence of a life field around living objects has been scientifically demonstrated. In Russia in the 1950s Semyon and Valentina Kirlian worked out a photographic process which enabled what has been identified as the aura to be photographed. Any healthy living organism when photographed by their special technique is seen to emit rays and sparks of light. What the Kirlians have done, and what has now been repeated in laboratories in other parts of the world, is to make visible electromagnetic waves just outside the range of normal human vision.

Some people indeed claim that, by looking out of the corner of the eye under special conditions of lighting, they can see another person's aura without any mechanical aids. Lyall Watson says, in his book *Supernature*: 'Those who claim to have seen the aura describe it as surrounding the body in a smooth egg shape, wider at the head than the feet.' In *The Teaching of Don Juan*, Carlos Castaneda states that his American Indian friend Don Juan, who is one of those who claim to be able to see the aura, asserts: 'Real people look like luminous eggs when you *see* them.'

Now the aura can also be detected by dowsing devices, the pendulum being the most suitable for the purpose. Having studied what various authors had to say about the aura, I decided to experiment with certain domestic animals. In practice the exercise presented some difficulties, for it is quite a lengthy proceeding and the animal, if awake, tends to become impatient. My experiments have therefore been conducted with animals at rest, including calves, sheep, cats and dogs.

In general, the field of influence, as discovered by the pendulum, begin at about 20in from the animal's body, which is what might be expected, 20in being the cord length for a pendulum reacting to organic matter. The oval shape of the human aura is presumably due to the most powerful waves emanating from the head. In humans standing erect the shape of the aura is that of an egg standing on its small end. The aura of animals is also egg-shaped, but with the egg lying on its side. As with humans, there is a wide part of the aura around the head, though the width is greater in animals with active brains, such as the dog and particularly the cat, than with placid herbivores such as the cow and sheep.

We now encounter yet another complication in this art or science of dowsing. Dowsing instruments can apparently take account of abstract ideas. The cord length for a male animal is 24in, but for a female animal 29in. The pendulum thus distinguishes between the sexes.

Unfortunately, those cord lengths coincide with those for certain concrete substances. For both masculinity and diamonds the cord length is 24in; for both femininity and gold the cord length is 29in. Lethbridge ruefully recounts an amusing incident — he got what he hoped was the reaction for gold but found instead a female beetle! Gold and diamonds are not really good subjects for the dowsing rod or pendulum.

In establishing the shape of the aura around an animal body one might expect to find the emanations strongest from the area of the sex organs, but this is not so. They seem to originate from the head; hence the egg-shaped aura.

Trees are other living entities difficult to investigate by dowsing, largely because they are usually surrounded by grass and/or other vegetation to which dowsing instruments give the same reaction. The best subject is probably the tree growing up from a suburban pavement and hence surrounded by concrete, asphalt or paving-stones. The pendulum and dowsing rod give a reaction as one approaches the trunk, but overhanging branches tend to confuse the issue.

North American Indians used to stand with their backs pressed against the trunks of certain trees to absorb the energy they believed to be pouring from the living wood. The

German Chancellor Bismarck is said to have adopted the same stance under an oak, half-an-hour a day. The recognition of a life force emanating from trees — and a benign influence at that — would thus seem to be widespread. There are, however, doubtless many more important facts to be learnt about it, and other dowsers, with more time at their disposal than I have so far been able to devote to it, may well find it a fruitful field for investigation.

5

Dowsing and Plants

In the last chapter, when describing the technique of analysing an area of ground, we saw that the gyrations of the pendulum with a cord length of 20in indicated the presence of organic matter, including vegetation. We now look more closely at the information that dowsing instruments can provide on plant life. To my mind this is one of the most fruitful investigations that a dowser can undertake; at least it is thoroughly practical.

The exercise is essentially a study of affinities or compatibilities. We will begin with the relationship of plants with soils. Every gardener knows how futile it is to try to grow, for instance, azaleas and rhododendrons in a lime-rich soil. An incompatibility exists between these plants and calcium. By dowsing we can establish the degree of compatibility between virtually any species, or even variety, of plant and any given soil. By experimenting with our dowsing instrument we can also determine what substances should be added to soils to make them more congenial to plants.

The technique is simple. On a board or table place any part of a plant as a sample — a leaf, fruit, bud, root or the entire plant. On the same flat surface place a sample of the soil, at say 20 or 30in from the plant. In one hand hold a *short* pendulum (cord length about 2—5in) between thumb and finger; in the other take a pointer (my wooden meat skewer serves nicely). Hold the pendulum over the soil and the tip of the pointer against the plant.

In due course the pendulum will start to oscillate. When it attains a strong movement move it slowly towards the plant. One of four things will soon happen: 1, the oscillations will increase; 2, the oscillations will continue with little change; 3, the pendulum will change its motion from oscillation to clockwise gyration; 4, the pendulum will change to anti-clockwise gyration.

The first reaction means that the soil and the plant are compatible — the more vigorous the oscillations the higher the degree of compatibility. The second implies that the plant can tolerate the soil without being particularly enamoured of it. The switch from oscillation to gyration indicates a deficiency in the soil, which can, however, be corrected. An anti-clockwise reaction for a dowser who normally obtains clockwise reactions is a statement of incompatibility, with little chance of correction.

Consideration of 2 and 3 above introduces the question of altering the composition of the soil to make it more compatible to the plant. Let us take as a specific example a problem very familiar to farmers. It is spring-time, and a field of barley has a decidedly yellow tinge instead of a healthy green. We place one of the barley plants on our operating table, 20 or 30in from a small pile of the field's soil, and test their compatibility with the short pendulum. The most probable reaction we shall get is a change from oscillation to gyration. The soil is deficient in something the plant needs.

We experiment first with the major plant nutrients, namely, nitrogen, potash and phosphates. While we continue to operate the pendulum a colleague slowly adds a nitrogenous fertiliser to the heap of soil. Soon the gyrations die down and the pendulum starts to oscillate again. Our assistant continues to pour on the nitrogen until the oscillations become really strong. Now we have a soil that is perfectly suited to the plant. A proportionate application of nitrogen to the soil of the field will restore the barley crop to health.

The example is, of course, a simple one. Any knowledgeable farmer would be able to diagnose nitrogen deficiency without taking all that trouble. It serves, however, to illustrate the technique. Potash and phosphate deficiency are less easy to determine, and trace-element deficiency is even more difficult.

Trace elements are chemical elements present in the soil in very small quantities yet nevertheless essential to healthy plant growth. A deficiency of boron in the soil, for instance, results in the tissues of roots such as turnips and swedes or the stalks of brassicas turning brown and starting to rot. The remedy is to add small amounts of borax or boracic powder to the soil. The pendulum can diagnose the deficiency and indicate the correct application of borax.

Other important trace elements include iron, magnesium, manganese, copper, zinc and molybdenum. Iron deficiency produces chlorosis, or lack of chlorophyll, in the leaves. So does magnesium, especially in tomatoes. Blotching and mottling of leaves, accompanied by stunted growth, can indicate manganese deficiency. Shortage of molybdenum in the soil is the commonest cause of the deformity known as 'whiptail' in cauliflowers. Plants may also fail through the absence of even small quantities of micronutrients such as iodine, cobalt, and vanadium.

All these deficiencies can be quite readily remedied. The sulphates of the several elements, such as magnesium sulphate, manganese sulphate, zinc sulphate and so on, are the compounds usually recommended, though a visit to the garden centre for some proprietary brand of plant food will generally solve the problem. The trouble is that once the results of the deficiencies are sufficiently pronounced to be obvious, the damage will have been done and will often be irreparable. Early diagnosis is therefore the best safeguard, and here dowsing can be of immense value.

Dowsing can also be used in the diagnosis of diseases and pests that afflict plants, but more of that in a later chapter. One point to be mentioned here, however, that leads us on to the next area of exploration of dowsing potential, is the presence of toxic substances in the soil. These too can, of course, be identified by the pendulum or rod, but apart from industrial pollution some toxic substances are manufactured by other plants. Usually they emanate from the roots, producing a soil highly incompatible to certain other species — which brings us to the study of affinities and incompatibilities between plants. It is a subject which I myself have found exceptionally interesting, and as I have never seen anything in print about it, from the point of view of dowsing, I propose to devote more space to it than might otherwise be justified.

46

Plant Affinities

The procedure for determining plant affinities is exactly the same as for establishing the compatibility or otherwise of plants with soils. We set the two plants to be tested on a flat surface, about 25in apart. The pendulum is held over one plant, the pointer directed at the other. When the pendulum starts to oscillate, move it slowly towards the second plant. If the oscillations increase in strength, the two plants are highly compatible. If the oscillations show little change, the two plants are tolerant or indifferent to each other. If the oscillations switch to gyrations the two are repelled by each other. The stronger the gyrations, or if they are anti-clockwise, the greater the antipathy.

The practical use of the information thus acquired is obvious. Two highly compatible plants will aid each other's growth and may occupy adjoining garden plots or share the same plot. Two antipathetic plants should never be grown near each other. Gardeners and horticultural scientists have done a considerable amount of work on the subject of companion plants, and I have used their findings as an indication of what to test. A splendid little book with a lot of information on the matter is *Companion Plants and How to Use Them* by Helen Philbrick and Richard B. Gregg (published in 1967), while that lovely little classic, *Old Wives' Lore for Gardeners*, by Maureen and Bridget Boland (1976), is also helpful. Guided by them I sat down at intervals throughout one summer with my pendulum and pointer.

Garlic seemed a good subject to start with, on the grounds that, being a pungently aromatic plant, it ought to arouse strong attractions or repulsions. Gardeners have long known that roses grown near garlic seem to develop a stronger perfume, and, sure enough, the pendulum indicated a high degree of compatibility between them. Garlic and beetroot also seemed quite strongly attracted to each other, and a less pronounced but still favourable reaction occurred between garlic and carrots. Garlic and beans (of several types) vigorously repelled each other.

I found this odd, because the pendulum showed a moderately favourable reaction between beans on the one hand and

47

beetroot and carrots on the other. Beans, in fact, seem compatible with most other vegetables, except onions, garlic and shallots but including leeks, even though they are members of the onion family. Having some plants of summer savory in the garden I tested them against both beans and garlic and found, somewhat to my surprise, that it was compatible with both. Clearly it must not be assumed that, because two plants are incompatible, all the plants which are compatible to the one will be incompatible to the other.

Experimenting further, I found that when I held the pendulum over a beetroot and used the pointer on a runner bean I obtained a favourable reaction, albeit a mild one. When I reversed the positions of the plants, however, holding the pendulum over the bean and the pointer against the beetroot, and moving the pendulum from the bean towards the beetroot, I got no reaction at all. I inferred that the runner bean derives some benefit from growing near beetroot but that the beetroot is more or less indifferent to the presence of the bean.

The following table embodies most of my findings to date:

	Plants which promote growth	Plants which inhibit growth
Bean (broad, French, runner and dwarf,	All brassicas; beetroot; carrot; celery; cucumber; marrow; squash; savory; strawberry; sweet corn; parsley; potato; leek	Onion; garlic; fennel; buttercup; gladiolus
Beetroot	Onions; garlic	Turnip; brassicas in general; cruciferous weeds
Asparagus	Parsley; tomato	
Brassicas (cabbage, savoy, cauliflower, broccoli, kohl rabi, calabrese, etc)	Potato; most herbs, especially sage and mint; celery	Tomato; strawberry; fennel
Carrot	Lettuce; chives; onion; leek; bean; pea; turnip	
Celery (also celeriac)	Bean; pea; tomato; leek; brassicas	

	Plants which promote growth	Plants which inhibit growth
Cucumber	Bean; brassicas; celery; lettuce; radish; sweet corn	
Leek	Carrot; celery; bean; pea; turnip	
Lettuce	Carrot; radish; strawberry	
Marrow (squash, etc)	Bean; celery; lettuce; radish; sweet corn	Potato
Onion	Beetroot; carrot; lettuce; camomile; savory	Bean; brassicas; strawberry
Potato	Bean; brassicas; pea; strawberry; nasturtium; horse-radish	Tomato; cucumber; marrow; raspberry; most herbs; sunflower
Pea	As bean, with the addition of turnip, radish and marigold	As bean
Radish	Lettuce; pea; carrot; nasturtium	
Spinach	Potato; strawberry	
Strawberry	Bean; borage; lettuce; onion; spinach; marigold; pine needles	Brassicas; potato; gladiolus
Sweet Corn	Bean; pea; cucumber; marrow; melon; potato	
Tomato	Asparagus; marigold; nettle; onion; parsley	Brassicas; potato; fennel
Turnip	Bean; carrot; pea; leek; parsley	Artemisia

Most vegetables seem to benefit from growing near most herbs, except dandelion. For several years I cultivated a garden the history of which extended back over centuries, probably to the time of the Dominican monks who had a priory nearby in the Middle Ages. In the borders lemon balm was abundant, and, tested with the pendulum, it seemed to be beneficial to almost every garden plant. I wonder whether the monks and their successors knew this and cultivated it deliberately.

WD&OD D

Checking several other herbs, I found that most of them were compatible with most vegetables, but that fennel was an exception; several vegetables did not approve of it. Rue and artemisia (formerly well known as wormwood) were also unpopular. Most gardeners know that a strong growth of nettles indicates a fertile soil, and the pendulum suggests that nettles are useful companion plants for a number of vegetables. They tend to bring out the flavour or essence of aromatic herbs.

Marigolds and parsley are both versatile plants, able to benefit a number of garden crops. Parsley is particularly compatible with beans, tomatoes and roses.

It is interesting that the gladiolus should have earned a few black marks, particularly with regard to beans and strawberries, for as a student of folklore I have come across gladiolus before. The belief that it is unlucky or unhealthy to take gladiolus into a sickroom seems to be quite widespread; and yet the gladiolus has not had a long history as a garden flower. A plant which is said to be very beneficial to other plants growing near it is hemp (cannabis), but for obvious reasons I have been unable to experiment with it.

When testing garden plants it is useful to have information about both compatible and incompatible species, but with wild plants, and notably those classified by gardeners as weeds, only the incompatible ones are of practical interest. I have tested a few common weeds, particularly couch-grass, and find that its growth is inhibited, according to the pendulum, by tomatoes, turnips and most leguminous plants. Nightshade of several species is encouraged by leguminous plants and also by sweet corn. Nasturtiums seem to have a detrimental effect on that troublesome weed ground elder (*Aegopodium podograria*).

The above is a summary of experiments carried out whenever I had time during four or five summer months. Obviously it just scratches the surface of what is manifestly a fascinating study. Much original work still remains to be done.

The investigation to this point, however, leads on to a nearly related subject. The pendulum is simply providing information about facts, about whether it is beneficial or detrimental to have this plant and that plant growing together; it tells us nothing about the reasons for those reactions. No doubt it could, if the constituents of the plants were to be separated and analysed, but that is a refinement which I must leave to some future investigator.

What has been established by other means is that certain plants do contain substances that are deleterious to others. Often these substances are present in the roots and from them seep into the soil, where they spread and affect the roots of neighbouring plants. Conifer trees in particular excrete considerable amounts of toxic substances into the soil, which is one of the reasons for the meagre muster of plants to be found growing under conifers. A poison excreted by buttercup roots has an inhibiting effect on leguminous plants, which accounts for the fact that a vigorous growth of clovers is never found in a pasture where buttercups flourish.

The distinguished archaeologist and dowser, the late T. C. Lethbridge, conducted an incomplete investigation into the properties of certain trees identified in folklore as lucky or unlucky. Using the short pendulum he tested them against himself for affinity. Increased oscillation of the pendulum as it was moved from over his left hand towards a sample of the tree indicated attraction or affinity; a change to gyration indicated repulsion or incompatibility. He obtained the following results:

Trees showing attraction or affinity to this human subject — rowan; oak; hawthorn; hazel; willow; apple; ivy; beech.

Trees showing repulsion or incompatibility — elder; elm; holly; ash; pine; fig.

Bearing in mind the folklore beliefs about the protective value of rowan (mountain ash, *Sorbus aucuparia*), he placed a sample of rowan against a sample of elder. Before the rowan was introduced the pendulum showed a strong antipathy between himself and the elder. Immediately the rowan was in position the gyrations ceased and oscillations were resumed. The rowan was evidently an interruptor, masking or counteracting the influence of the elder, in the same way as certain minerals act as interruptors, as described on page 38. His conclusion there was that interruptors were a bit of a nuisance, preventing us from discovering concealed objects. Here, if folklore has any value as a guide, the interruptor is benign, protecting us from the noxious influence of a hostile entity.

In compiling my encyclopedia of folklore, *In Search of Lost Gods*, I was impressed by the mass of ancient beliefs about trees. Rowan was considered a very beneficent tree, offering protection against witchcraft and the evil eye. Rowan trees were for this reason planted by farmsteads and rowan branches nailed above the doors. Cows were given collars of rowan when visiting the bull, doubtless to assist conception; pigs wore similar collars to make them grow quickly.

Oak was a sacred tree which was supposed to give protection against lightning. In pagan times weddings were celebrated under sacred oaks. Bonfires at special seasonal festivals had to be made of oak and rowan. Twigs of hawthorn hung over a doorway were considered a protection against witches; over a cowshed door they ensured a good milk supply. Maypoles, around which fertility dances were engaged in on May Day, were usually of hawthorn, which in Greek mythology was the emblem of Persephone, who married Pluto, god of the underworld, but who returned to earth every spring, bringing a revival of life after winter.

Hazel, strongly associated with dowsing, was widely regarded as a benevolent plant. Crossed hazel wands on the chest of a corpse were supposed to be a protection against evil spirits in the other world. Apple trees were regarded with such respect that a special wassailing ceremony was devised to do them honour and to prevail on them to produce a good crop. It is still practised in a few places. Apples were widely used in divination, and to fell an apple tree was considered unlucky. There are similar beneficient associations for willow, ivy and beech.

Of the 'bad' trees, on the other hand, elder has a particularly evil reputation. It is very unlucky to burn elder wood or even to have it indoors. Anyone falling asleep under an elder tree puts himself in the power of witches. It was considered dangerous to be near an elder tree after dark. Real blood was shed by an elder cut on Midsummer Eve. Holly was a witch tree, and anyone cutting it does so at his peril. Even today holly trees are often left standing when a hedge is trimmed. A holly hedge is a protection against witches, and so is a threshold of holly wood. The folklore associations of ash, fig and pine are more nebulous, but elm is said 'to hate mankind'.

It is intriguing to find the dowsing pendulum providing some apparent confirmation of this ancient lore. The witch motif is explained by the belief that trees possessed a spirit or personality of their own, with which a competent witch could exchange at will. It was not therefore really the tree which was hostile to humanity but the malignant spirit of the witch that had invaded the tree. There is a medieval record of a Welsh wizard or 'priest' who was taken to London and burned at the stake, together with the wooden idol which bore the same name as himself. The wizard and the idol (shaped from a tree) were thus held to have a common identity. One can appreciate that trees considered sacred by a pagan religion would acquire an opposite reputation when Christianity became dominant. But why were they considered sacred in the first place? Is there some natural antipathy between certain trees and human beings that calls, in terms of religious ideology, for propitiation? The dowsing pendulum suggests that there may be.

Lethbridge further discovered, by the method described on page 77, that all trees showing an attraction to or affinity with humans gave a reaction to the test for the female principle, while the antipathetic or hostile ones were all male. This has no obvious connection with the actual sex of the trees, most of which bear both male and female flowers. The information has a meaning which so far eludes us.

6

Dowsing and Insects

As the toxic substances released by certain plants adversely affect certain other plants nearby, it is reasonable to expect that they have a similar or even more pronounced effect on insect life. And so it proves. Put another way, the presence of certain plants is incompatible with the well-being of certain insects and other forms of life. This, too, is a matter which can be tested by the pendulum.

Place the insect and the plant 20 or 30in apart on a flat surface, as when investigating the affinities of plants. Hold the pendulum over the insect and direct the pointer to the plant. When the pendulum has developed good oscillations over the insect move it slowly towards the plant and interpret its reactions as for plant affinities.

I expected more difficulty with making this experiment than in fact occurred. I reasoned that a dead insect would probably not do; the experiment would have to be made with a live one. Live insects move about, some of them pretty smartly, and to confine them in a glass container seemed to risk getting a false reading; there was a danger, I argued, that the glass would be tested as well as, or instead of, the insect. In practice I found no difference between live and dead insects. The pendulum reacted to both alike.

The findings were much as might be expected. I found a compatibility between aphids on the one hand and roses and beans on the other. Antipathy, however, existed between aphids and nasturtiums and between aphids and nettles. The pendulum showed a decided incompatibility between ants and plants of the mint family, and the same plants tend to repel the cabbage-white butterfly (I used its caterpillars for the test) and also the flea-beetle. Flea-beetles and lettuce do not like each other. Carrot-fly are repelled by onions. Honey bees, however, are greatly attracted to lemon balm.

Such an investigation need not, of course, be confined to animate things. It is just as easy to test an insect against a mineral substance or chemical compound. For example, place a slug on a flat surface and test it against a heap of salt. As the pendulum, oscillating, is moved from the slug towards the salt the oscillations change to strong gyrations. Salt, as we are well aware, is fatal to slugs, and the pendulum confirms it. The test can be used to check on the effectiveness of proprietary compounds against the pests they are advertised to kill.

The door thus opens on a much wider study. Most diseases are caused by living creatures, either animal or vegetable (we make an exception of viruses, because it is at present uncertain whether they should be regarded as animal, vegetable or mineral). There is thus no essential difference between discovering, by means of the pendulum, that salt is anathema to slugs and that applications of lime may be used to control the fungus disease club-root (*Plasmodiophora*).

That indefatigable investigator, the late T. C. Lethbridge, discovered that the pendulum could provide us with much more information about insects and their food. Studying his discoveries with the long pendulum, he was struck by the inconvenience of having so many substances or concepts possessing the same cord length or 'rate'. The 'rate' 22in was a good example. Silver, lead, calcium, sodium and the colour grey all reacted to it, while magnesium, potassium and magnetism were very near. Surely there ought to be a way of differentiating between them?

He did so by counting the number of gyrations made by the pendulum. We can easily repeat his experiment and check his findings. Approach a piece of silver, reposing on a flat surface, with a pendulum oscillating (cord length 22in). When over the silver the motion will change to gyrations. Count the number of gyrations before the pendulum reverts to oscillations. You will find it is 22.

Now repeat the experiment over a lump of lead, and you will

discover that the number of gyrations is only 18; with sodium it is 36, with calcium 30. The colour grey provokes only 7 gyrations. So Lethbridge worked out that a pendulum with a cord length of 22in making 22 gyrations indicated the presence of silver, and he wrote down the 'rate' for silver as '22:22'.

He now turned his attention to organic matter. Grass, he found, reacted to a cord length or 'rate' of 16in. With a cord of that length the pendulum, gyrating over grass, made 18 circles. The 'rate' for grass was thus written '16:18'. Cow dung, being composed largely of grass, also reacted to the 16-in cord length, but the pendulum made 36 gyrations. The 'rate' for cow dung was thus '16:36'. Lethbridge then extracted some dung-beetles and their grubs from the cow dung and tested them. They gave the rate 16:36, exactly the same as for the dung.

This was a highly important discovery: it seemed to establish a precise relationship between an insect and its food. Lethbridge followed it up with a detailed examination of a range of specimens of plant-eating beetles of the genus *Chrysomela*, which he happened to have, and their food plants. He tested ten species of *Chrysomela*, and each had the same rate as its food plant. Thus, *Chrysomela banksi* and its food plant *Lamium* (the deadnettle) both had the rate 12:18; *Chrysomela menthrasti* and its food plant *Mentha* (mint) had the rate 12:22; and so on. All the *Chrysomela* beetles responded to a cord length of 12, except one, *Chrysomela hyperici*, which reacted to a cord length of 13. As suggested by its specific name, this insect feeds on the plant *Hypericum* (St John's wort). Both insect and plant have the rate 13:13.

It looks as though this affinity, almost identity, between the insect and its food-plant is universal and that a table could be prepared cataloguing them all. It calls for another Linnaeus to make it a life work. From some experimental checks I have found no discrepancies. However, the determining factor would seem to be the plant not the insect. All insects feeding on the same plants seem to respond to the same rate. Lethbridge found this with his dung-beetles. It made no difference whether they belonged to the genera *Aphodius*, *Geotrupes* or *Onthophagus*; they all responded to the rate 16:36, which is that for cow dung.

What is the significance of this? The pendulum is not manufacturing evidence: it is reacting to something that exists. It seems that each plant is emitting some kind of wave, force, current, beam (call it what you will) which both the pendulum and the insects concerned can pick up. The insects are apparently programmed to home in on it, much as a plane is directed by radar signals. One of the mysteries of nature could thus be at least partially explained.

Some of the beetles investigated by Lethbridge confined their activities to one food plant only. Both the beetle and the food plant were rare in quite a number of instances. That is a common arrangement. One example of which I have had some experience is the black mullein (*Verbascum nigrum*), a rare plant growing chiefly on chalk and limestone soils. In July and August the attractive, spotted caterpillars of the striped lychnis moth (*Cucullia lychnitis*) feed on the flowers and unripe seed capsules of this plant. I have more than once found a colony of caterpillars gorging themselves on an isolated small group of black mullein plants, miles away — as far as I could ascertain — from any other specimens, and I have wondered how the moths located the food plant when they wished to lay their eggs. The dowsing pendulum indicates a method. Once a moth picked up a beam and locked its navigation gear on it, distance would be no object.

The phenomenon suggests the possibility that animal migration in general may be explained in the same way. All that is needed is to postulate that a *place* as well as a plant can emit a beam, force or current that can be picked up by any creature properly programmed. Birds, butterflies, animals and fish undertake tremendous journeys to arrive accurately at a pinpointed location. Swallows will make an aerial voyage of ten thousand miles, swoop into a familiar barn and alight on the beam that supported their nest in the preceding year. Monarch butterflies in California return to hibernate each winter on the same tree, which is so densely covered by them that it appears to be bearing a strange crop of leaves. Salmon cross the oceans to the estuary, the river, the tributary and the gravelly spawning grounds favoured by untold generations of salmon. And the many instances of dogs, cats and other domestic animals returning to their old homes from places scores or hundreds of miles away are capable of a similar explanation.

We ourselves possess what may be termed 'the homing instinct' to some degree. It is most pronounced in primitive and unsophisticated people, who seldom 'get lost'. But most of us tend to move faster and with more assurance when we are going towards home, even when travelling by a circuitous route in unfamiliar territory.

7

Dowsing, Health and Disease

The techniques of dowsing already described can be employed in any further research we may choose to undertake. The chief problem is to determine how best to apply them. Let us go a little further with the study of affinities and compatibilities.

With the short pendulum we have tested a slug against a heap of salt and found that, as we already knew, they are highly incompatible! When the pendulum, nicely oscillating, is moved towards the salt its motion changes to strong gyrations. (It is advisable to stress again that each dowser must establish for himself the pattern for normal reactions. I and perhaps most dowsers get oscillations switching to gyrations, but for some dowsers the opposite is true.) Replace the salt by a heap of proprietary slug pellets, and the reaction will be the same as with salt. Replace those, however, with a lettuce leaf, and the pendulum will record a perfect compatibility. Now switch the positions of the slug and the lettuce leaf, so that the pendulum is suspended over the lettuce and the pointer is directed at the slug. The reaction of the pendulum now indicates incompatibility. The lettuce may be good for the slug, but the slug is certainly not good for the lettuce!

I once conducted a somewhat similar experiment with a cat — a nice, fat contented cat who had recently enjoyed a good meal and was therefore prepared to remain asleep while I was busy over her. I tested her first against a poison bait that had been set out for mice, and predictably the pendulum indicated a strong antipathy between the two. Then for the poison bait I substituted a dead mouse which I had reason to believe had succumbed to the same poison. Sure enough, I obtained the same reaction; the mouse would have been bad for the cat. The cat, of course, would have instinctively known that and would have left the mouse alone, but it was interesting to have the pendulum's confirmation. The technique could be used for tracing the persistence of deadly organo-chlorides, which have been causing such heavy mortality among wild birds, in the bodies of creatures which have been feeding on poisoned creatures, all the way down a long chain.

Enlisting the aid of a young assistant, I tested her against both the poison and the mouse. The pendulum assured me that she would be allergic to both. Further testing against a variety of foods, however, proved that she had a healthy constitution, capable of digesting anything within reason.

I conducted some experiments on myself. This technique can be a little tricky, but I find that I can get reasonably consistent results by holding the pendulum in my right hand over my left hand until it works up some strong oscillations and then moving it cautiously towards a sample of the substance under test. The pendulum pleasantly confirmed that I can eat such diverse foods as bread, eggs, meat, honey, butter and vegetables with impunity and even with benefit. Onions, however, were an exception for they gave a mild, adverse reaction, thus confirming what I am well aware of, that raw onions are inclined to give me indigestion. But when for the raw onions I substituted a large, well-boiled one all was well. I can eat boiled onions with no ill effects.

I next tested myself against a series of patent medicines. A word of caution is appropriate here, for the diagnosing and treatment of disease is a medical matter, and much harm can sometimes result from trying to treat oneself. Nevertheless, remedies for colds, backaches, headaches, constipation and other common ailments abound in every chemist's shop, and the family cupboard without an assortment of them must be a rarity. So I thought I would find out just how effective some of them are.

Using the same technique as before, I assumed that, as with food, if the medicine was likely to do me good the oscillations of the pendulum would increase as I moved it towards the medicine bottle or container. If it was likely to have little effect on my health, the oscillations would slow down or change to gentle gyrations. If it was likely to be harmful, the gyrations would be strong. I found none that was definitely harmful but very few that were beneficial either! Most of them seemed to be entirely neutral. There was no point in my spending money on them. Still, the same may not be true for everyone. One man's meat is another's poison.

A competent dowser with a pendulum would have been an invaluable asset to those ancient monarchs who felt it necessary to employ tasters as a protection against attempts to poison them. As we have seen, experienced dowsers have no difficulty in establishing the toxicity of a plant or a substance. If old King Mithridates had been subjected to a dowsing examination, however, he would have yielded decidedly abnormal results. It will be remembered that he is said to have developed immunity to all known poisons by incorporating at first minute, and then increasing, quantities of them in his food, so that in the end he was immune to them all. If you or I were to test ourselves against, for instance, arsenic, the pendulum would give a violent adverse reaction. With Mithridates, however, if the stories are true, it would have shown a mild compatibility. There was so much arsenic in his body that the pendulum would have recognised an affinity.

This technique can be useful in uncovering veiled toxins. It may possibly have been known and employed in prehistoric times. How did men first discover which berries and plants were poisonous and which good to eat? Did successive generations experiment, with series of unpleasant or even fatal results, until the matter was at last well established? Perhaps it happened like that. Examination of the stomach contents of the Bronze Age men whose bodies have been preserved in the bogs of Denmark reveals that a wide range of seeds, much wider than we would eat today, were consumed in a kind of gruel or broth. Later ages discarded many of the less nutritious, retaining wheat, barley, rye and certain other grasses. Did early men conduct a similarly wide spectrum of experiments with wild fruits, enduring the casualties caused by eating the attractive berries of deadly nightshade and the discomforts resulting from a dose of buckthorn berries? Or were they able to take short cuts, by means of some dowsing technique?

61

Let us pursue the study of diet a little further. For the convenience of my wife, who likes to get her cooking done in the mornings, we normally have our main meal around midday, a good, well-balanced one, consisting of meat, vegetables, dessert and all the accessories. Testing myself one day against an appetising plateful, I found that it and myself were highly compatible! But when, for the sake of experiment, I tested myself against a similar plateful an hour or so later, I got an adverse reaction! The second dinner and I were definitely not going to agree.

Finding a glass of table wine taken with a meal helps my digestion, I am mindful of St Paul's advice — take a little wine for your stomach's sake. I pour out a glass of wine and test my reactions to it by moving the oscillating pendulum from a position over my left hand towards the wine. All is well. But when I replace the glass of wine by a full bottle the pendulum falters and switches to gyrations. If someone pours wine into a large jug while I continue dowsing with the pendulum, I can gradually increase the strength of the gyrations. The quality of the wine may be excellent and beneficial, but the quantity is wrong. To drink a whole bottleful would do me no good.

An adaptation of this technique could, it seems, enable a man to determine when he had drunk too much to pass a police breathalyser test: or it could even be used by policemen as an alternative to breathalysing!

One of the commonest disorders among cattle is hypomagnesaemia or grass tetany, which causes digestive upsets and sometimes mortality among cattle turned out to graze on lush spring grass. It results from an imbalance in the mineral content of the grass, which is, among other things, deficient in magnesium and has an excess of potassium. The incidence of the disorder has increased considerably in the past few decades, owing to the practice of using one-species pastures, the species usually being perennial rye-grass. When I was farming I used to counteract the tendency by including in every new pasture a series of herb strips. The herbs, primarily chicory, yarrow, ribwort plantain and dandelion, possessed deep roots which could tap mineral reserves in the subsoil. Today the condition is usually corrected by feeding mineral supplements to the cattle.

Grass tetany is now so well known to farmers that they quickly recognise the symptoms and take remedial action. Years ago, when it was not so common, I have more than once forestalled it by the aid of the pendulum. It was simply a matter of analysing grass samples, noting the deficiencies and adding various substances until a satisfactory balance was reached.

If by testing myself against raw onions I can diagnose the cause of the indigestion from which I am suffering, is it possible to determine the nature of disease caused by microbial infection? Of course. Some privileged dowsers, including the celebrated French Abbé Bouly, have been able to obtain such diagnoses by testing human patients against bacterial preparations. The pendulum or rod will indicate when the bacillus culture coincides with the one from which the patient is suffering. Not many dowsers, however, have access to such facilities.

It is also possible to pinpoint a diseased organ by direct dowsing. Hold the short pendulum between thumb and one finger of one hand and with the index finger of the other hand point in turn to the various organs of the body. Teeth provide a convenient example. As the testing proceeds, the pendulum will oscillate at a regular rhythm until a decaying tooth is reached. Then the movement will switch to gyration.

Similar reactions can be expected from examinations of other parts of the body. It is best to have the subject lying first supine and then prone, so that the body can be thoroughly and methodically examined. Some dowsers modify the normal technique by holding the pendulum over one of the hands of the subject and exploring the body with the forefinger of the other hand.

As with other aspects of dowsing, the reaction of the pendulum varies with individual dowsers. Many, perhaps most, dowsers get oscillations over healthy tissues and gyrations over diseased parts, but with others the reactions are reversed. Thorough tests must therefore be made, to determine what are his normal reactions, before any dowser starts serious work. Once they have been established, however, they can be relied on.

Sexing

A related operation is the sexing of eggs, which is said to be still carried out commercially in Japan. The general assumption seems to be that the pendulum swings backwards and forwards — the usual oscillatory motion — over an egg containing a male chick and gyrates over that holding a female embryo. W. H. Trinder had considerable success when holding first a cock's feather and then a hen's feather in his hand against the cord of the pendulum.

When he obtained a reaction with a cock's feather in his hand he set that egg aside as being definitely male; when there was no reaction the egg could be either female or sterile. He then tested the second lot of eggs with a hen's feather in his hand. Those which reacted were female, those which did not were sterile. He was 100 per cent right with small numbers of eggs, but when he tried the technique on larger quantities, for use in an incubator, his success rate fell to 90 per cent. This margin of error he attributed, probably correctly, to fatigue. Time and again, in other spheres as well as this, failure has followed attempts by a dowser to work when he is tired or when he tries to do too much in one session. I myself have achieved a reasonable success with sexing hens' eggs in the days when we used to set broody hens to hatch chicks. I could manage the thirteen or fourteen eggs that made up the conventional sitting but have not attempted it with larger numbers.

The exercise is, of course, almost identical with what thousands of families must have lightheartedly practised — trying to determine the sex of an unborn child. The pendulum in such instances is usually a wedding ring on a thread. The generally accepted rule is that when the pendulum is suspended over the pregnant mother's body, oscillations indicate that the baby will be a boy, gyrations a girl — though here again the dowser should check over known objects, to make sure he is not one of those individuals for whom the pendulum gives reverse reactions. A word of caution must be given, and this operation regarded with reservations, because — as I see it — the dominant influence on the pendulum will be the mother herself, thus weighting the chances heavily towards a female reaction. The farther the pregnancy is advanced, the better the chances of obtaining a meaningful reaction, I would think.

T. C. Lethbridge, engaging in his highly original research, discovered that with the long pendulum there are definite cord lengths for masculinity and femininity. As we saw in chapter 4, for males the cord length or 'rate' is 24in, which happens to be the same as for diamonds; for females it is 29in, which is the same as for gold. This is one of the reasons why dowsing for gold is such a tricky operation. But more of this later.

Underground Streams and Health

We return now for a moment to the business of water divining, with which our investigation began. Here too we discover a medical connection. There seems to be a lot of evidence to link underground streams with certain forms of ill-health. The sort of evidence that has accumulated runs along the following lines: Mrs Arbuckle has suffered for years from arthritis or headaches or insomnia, coupled with bad dreams. A dowser discovers that an underground stream passes beneath the house and that Mrs Arbuckle's bed is sited exactly over its course. The bed is moved to another room, and Mrs Arbuckle's health rapidly improves.

That is precisely what once happened in my own household. My wife had been sleeping badly, frequently awakened in the early hours by nightmares, then finding it difficult to get to sleep again, and consequently starting the next day with a headache. She is more susceptible than I am to occult influences, so we changed places in bed. Her nights were less disturbed, though she still had uneasy dreams, and so did I. With the dowsing rod I had established that a strong dowsing field (presumably an underground stream, though we will return to that later) ran under the house, immediately under her side of the bed. As we were evidently both affected to some extent, we moved the bed to the other side of the room and were soon enjoying more peaceful sleep.

Some dowsers have even traced a link between underground streams and cancer. Living and sleeping for long periods directly over a subterranean stream can foster the development of cancer, they say. More details of some of the more outstanding research programmes are given in Chapter 13. Some claim that the connection between ill-health and underground streams was well known to our ancestors, who carefully avoided building houses on such sites. This I doubt. As I write, I am living in a house which is approximately 300 years old and is on a site where a house stood at least as early as the beginning of the sixteenth century, and yet a strong underground stream flows beneath it.

In writing this book I have confined myself as far as possible to matters of which I have had personal experience. In this question of the deleterious effects of underground water we are moving into territory where so far I have had to rely largely on the testimony of other dowsers, though I hope in due course to improve on that situation. Let us summarise the phenomena which, it is claimed, occur over subterranean streams.

1 People who spend much time living, and particularly sleeping, over such streams as indicated by dowsing instruments frequently suffer from insomnia, rheumatism, arthritis and other ailments and from general ill-health, and are more liable to contract cancer.

2 Farm animals housed in buildings on such sites also display symptoms of ill-health.

3 Domestic and laboratory animals confined to pens over underground streams display neurotic tendencies. Mice and rats under such conditions will become very aggressive and indulge in cannibalism.

4 Animals, given the choice, will always avoid such zones. When kept in a pen of which part is over an underground stream and part over an unaffected zone, they will always choose to sleep or rest in the latter. This contention can be tested through observation of the family dog or cat, which will have its own favourite sleeping-quarters and may deliberately avoid certain quarters of the house. Tested with rod or pendulum, the areas thus avoided will almost certainly be found to be over an underground current.

5 Preserved food, including jam, keeps badly when stored over an underground stream (so do vegetables).

6 Wine and cider do not keep well in such a location.

7 Some species of trees show evidence of disease when growing over underground streams. Apple trees tend to develop canker. Pears, plums and beeches do not thrive. On the other hand, certain other species seem to benefit from being located over a spring. They include oak, willow, poplar, elm and that tree of unidentified species which I found growing over a strong spring in northern Ghana (see page 13). Some vegetables appreciate these zones, while others are adversely affected.

8 Trees growing over underground streams are more likely to be struck by lightning.

9 Ants and termites seem to site their hills deliberately over underground streams and to benefit from the practice.

10 Colonies of bees whose hives are sited over underground streams flourish and grow strong. When swarming, the queen will choose a branch or other feature above a dowsing zone.

One conclusion apparent from the above list is that while the presence of underground streams is harmful to most higher forms of life (eg animals and humans) it is beneficial to many lower forms, such as insects and bacteria. The facts that jam and stored vegetables do not keep well and that wine and cider turn sour may be explained by the proliferation of bacteria in the affected zone. The prevalence of canker in apple trees seems analogous to the tendency of cancer to develop in human beings. The microbes which cause disease in the human body may well derive benefit from the presence of a dowsing zone.

But what possible reason can there be for underground water to produce such effects? Perhaps it is not the water itself which is responsible but the friction produced by its flow. In the 1930s, French dowsers using electrical equipment discovered concentrations of ions in the air above subterranean zones indicated by the dowsing rod. Their presence is now established by more sophisticated and advanced apparatus (this phenomenon is known as telluric radiation). The locations in which they occur are described as telluric zones. In instances which have been studied in depth a definite relationship has been established between them and the incidence of cancer.

Further details of these phenomena and the latest research into them are given in Chapter 13.

The function of dowsing is to provide information. Dowsing rods and pendulums can assist us to locate underground water, mineral ores and concealed objects. They can supply us with information about compatible and incompatible substances. They can, as we shall see in a later chapter, supply positive or negative answers to questions.

In the realm of health, from this stage it is a small step to supplying a corrective. If, for instance, we find by dowsing that a plant is suffering from a deficiency of boron or cobalt in the soil, the obvious course of action is to supply the missing element, and the correct quantities may also be established with the aid of a dowsing instrument. If we are able to identify the pollen which is causing hay fever, we can be given an injection to counteract the effects. If we can identify a poison, an antidote can be speedily prescribed. If an illness is caused by germs, we can obtain the correct medicine to kill them. To that extent dowsing has a medical application. But can dowsing be used actually to effect a cure? What can perhaps be considered a marginal example is provided by healing springs. While instances have been quoted of the deleterious consequences to men and animals of sleeping or living over certain underground streams, not all subterranean water has that effect. Many dowsers differentiate between beneficial and 'black' springs. We have already discussed some examples of 'black' springs; we need not look far for examples of beneficial ones. The reputed curative properties of the hot springs of Bath have been known since at least Roman times. The same belief in the healing powers of spring water impregnated with minerals (or something else?) lies behind the prosperity of every spa. The Biblical story of the pool of Bethesda, where 'an angel went down at a certain season into the pool and troubled the water; whosoever then first after the troubling of the water stepped in was made whole of whatsoever disease he had', is matched by the traditions associated with Loch na Naire in Sutherland, Scotland. Here the critical times were between midnight and 1 am on Lammas Day and May Day, when the water was said to have magical medicinal properties. The waters of Lourdes are a modern example.

Some waters were reputed to be effective against specific diseases. St Winifred's Well at Holywell, Denbighshire, was said to be particularly efficacious in curing nervous disorders; the Rag Well, at Walton, Yorkshire, for treating diseases of the eyes; the well at Altarnun, Cornwall, for healing lunatics; St Keverne's Well, Cornwall, for ensuring fertility; the well of St George, Denbighshire, for curing horses. Logically, such wells were regarded with reverence. In pre-Christian days they were held to be sacred to certain gods or goddesses or to have their resident nymphs. Their reputation has in many instances been preserved into Christian times. The church at Holybourne, Hampshire, is built over a sacred well. In the Derbyshire villages of Tissington, Wirksworth and others the holy wells are elaborately decorated for an Ascensiontide ritual, when they are blessed by the clergy. The number of holy wells in Britain alone runs into hundreds. A survey of those in Wales, probably incomplete, lists 1,179 wells, while sample surveys, very doubtfully comprehensive, of holy wells in English counties reveal between 20 and 70 per county.

Any proficient dowser in early times could have located these wells, though how one distinguished between beneficial and malignant water I have not yet been able to discover (apart from the positive/negative exercises with the pendulum described in a later chapter). A downward dip of the pointer of the forked twig indicates polluted water to dowsers for whom a normal reaction is a lift of the rod, but that reveals simply physical pollution, as by sewage. The difference between harmful waters, which produce malaise and illness in creatures living above them, and curative waters, which can effect healing, is more profound than that caused by contamination with unpleasant substances. It has to do with the nature of the electromagnetic radiation or whatever it is that emanates from the water. On page 93 is a description of how a dowser, A. D. Manning, has set about neutralising harmful emanations.

The practice of medicine can be conveniently divided into two categories, homoeopathy and allopathy. Homoeopathy is concerned with the general health of an organism, be it man or animal. Allopathy is concerned with the diagnosis and treatment of specific disease. It is hardly necessary to state that modern medicine, as practised in Western countries, falls into the second category. The first can be illustrated by the arrangement reputed to have prevailed in classical China, whereby a person paid the doctor as long as he enjoyed good health but collected compensation from the doctor if he fell ill!

In the sphere of allopathy the dowser can of course perform a useful diagnostic service. He can pinpoint the source of ill-health and can identify diseased or malfunctioning organs. The pendulum is the most convenient instrument to employ. W. H. Trinder's method of locating a decaying tooth has already been described. Distinguished medical dowsers, notably certain French abbés, have employed the same method for diagnosing disease in other parts of the body.

Since the 1930s numbers of researchers have experimented with diagnostic devices known as 'black boxes'. Inside the boxes are assemblages of wires and dials, and the insertion of a sample from the subject's body, such as a drop of blood or a hair, enables a diagnosis to be recorded. This branch of dowsing has been given the name 'radionics'. The contents of the 'black boxes' vary, and although they have been proved helpful, in perhaps many instances, they have to be considered as no more than aids to diagnosis. A proficient dowser can probably do just as well without them. My own experience with them being limited, I preserve an open mind.

In homoeopathy, too, dowsing plays a diagnostic role, though here it has a wider scope. Some of its possible activities have been described. For instance, an ailing plant is tested with a pendulum to determine what is lacking in its environment, ie the soil, and therefore what must be supplied to restore it to full health. The same technique can be applied to animals and humans. In the matter of diet, the pendulum can indicate the compatibility between certain types and quantities of food and an individual human body. Toxic substances as well as beneficial foods can be identified.

Many people who are attracted to the homoeopathic approach to health tend to place great value on herbal medicines, and with these too it is easy to establish affinities and incompatibilities. Nevertheless, it is important to recognise that homoeopathy is not dowsing. Dowsing can indicate what is wrong but cannot itself put it right.

There are, however, other factors than a correct physical balance involved in the maintenance of good health. It is a truism that a high proportion of illnesses have a connection with the mental state of the sufferer. A man who has been having frequent rows with his wife and has now lost his job is a sitting target for whatever infections may be circulating at the time. This, of course, is where allopathy tends to break down. A busy doctor may prescribe the correct medicine for the treatment of the infection, and the treatment may eradicate it, but it can do nothing to alleviate the man's mental stress. If he is still depressed by the loss of his job and filled with resentment against his wife it will not be long before he contracts some other ailment. He will be like the man in Christ's parable who, having had a devil cast out of him, almost immediately finds himself with seven other devils worse than the first.

A busy general practitioner, with his waiting-room filled with patients, will probably be unable to devote the necessary time for a lengthy interview to determine what really is wrong with the patient. A psychologist with more time at his disposal can do it. So can a dowser, using the positive/negative technique with a pendulum, provided he is intelligent enough to ask the right questions.

Beyond all this lie unexplored realms which dowsing is just beginning to reveal. Readers who have followed the discussion so far will now be aware of auras and cones, electromagnetic emanations and radiation and telluric zones, of which our other senses tell us nothing. Our behaviour, attitudes and health are influenced by things we see, hear, feel and smell. It is reasonable to assume, therefore, that those other factors in our environment which are revealed by our mysterious sixth sense will have an equal effect on us. We are just beginning to learn a little about how we react to them.

As an instance of the way which one line of thought is following, T. C. Lethbridge, investigating ghosts and other 'supernatural manifestations', suggests in his book *Ghosts and Divining Rod* that 'bundles of thoughts in an electro-magnetic field may possibly have a real existence for a time of their own. If that is so, mankind can create devils; but they will be of his own making.' In the USA a distinguished engineer, Edward Jastram, has been studying cases of dramatic personality changes, as for instance when a respectable, devout woman suddenly becomes coarse, foul-mouthed and addicted to drink. Dowsing by pendulum in such a case, Jastram discovered 'the presence of three alien personalities on board, very negative in character'. When these had been banished, the woman resumed her former personality.

The phenomenon was very similar to that described in the New Testament as possession by devils. Christ was able to 'cast out devils', but found it an exhausting process. When, as he was being jostled on every side by crowds of people, a woman with a persistent haemorrhage touched the edge of his garment and was healed, he enquired, 'Who touched me?', adding, 'Somebody touched me, for I felt that power went out from me.' So great was the drain on his energy that, after days spent in healing, he needed to spend whole nights on the mountainsides at prayer, recharging his batteries.

So it can be with dowsers who try to extend their operations from diagnosis to healing. They find themselves supplying the energy requirements which their patient lacks. As Tom Graves says in his book *Dowsing Techniques and Applications*, 'A disproportionate number of fringe practitioners have died in their early forties, having effectively burnt themselves out.'

8
Dowsing and the Fourth Dimension

The title of this chapter in the original version of the book was 'Dowsing and the Supernatural'. It was altered to avoid misunderstanding. Some readers would have objected that all dowsing is supernatural, but that depends on the definition of the word. *The Concise Oxford Dictionary* defines *supernatural* as 'due to or manifesting some agency above the forces of nature', and that certainly does *not* apply to dowsing.

Dowsing is entirely natural. It is the exercise of an additional sense, as real and natural as the more generally recognised senses of sight, hearing, scent, touch and taste. These familiar senses are means by which information about our environment is conveyed to our brain. Dowsing supplies our brain with an extra batch of data. It is not well understood and only now is it beginning to be given proper investigation and study, but it is not supernatural by that definition.

Nuttall's Standard Dictionary, however, defines 'supernatural' as 'being beyond or exceeding the known power of laws of nature; effected by agents, agencies or in ways which transcend the ordinary', and that comes somewhere near to describing dowsing. Further, this dictionary defines 'the supernatural' as 'the unseen, mysterious spiritual force or power that everywhere underlies and works in nature', and in later chapters we are driven back on some such explanation for certain dowsing phenomena. For the moment, though, we will set aside broader issues and concentrate on one new aspect of dowsing: a fourth dimension, taken to mean *time*.

Our study so far has been concerned mainly with tangible things, the existence of which can be confirmed by one or more of our other senses. Having located by dowsing techniques an underground source of water we can dig down and demonstrate that the water is there. Dowsing for minerals is undertaken for the very practical purpose of locating substances which we value and intend to use. The establishment of affinities and compatibilities between plants, or between plants and mineral substances (such as fertilisers), or between animals and plants, or animals (including humans) and mineral substances, simply achieves by dowsing the results which can be obtained, though perhaps less easily, by other means. We can learn by experiment, for instance, that a certain plant is dying for lack of nitrogen, or that henbane berries are deadly poisonous for us, or how much whisky we can safely drink. One of the few new phenomena we have encountered by dowsing alone is the existence of auras and cones, and even these are now being investigated by other scientific techniques.

What we are now going to examine is the use of dowsing in extending the frontier of knowledge into new territory. And a useful starting point is the investigation of errors in the findings of individual dowsers.

Time and again in previous chapters the importance has been stressed of each dowser determining for himself his personal reaction in each field investigated. For example, before he can obtain any valid information from a pendulum he has to discover whether for him gyrations are normally clockwise or anticlockwise and under what circumstances oscillations switch to gyrations and back again. Before he even begins a serious study he has to undertake a thorough series of preliminary tests. Once he has satisfied himself as to what is normal for him, he then, in many fields of study, has to proceed by trial and error. In establishing affinities and compatibilities, for instance, he has to test his subject against a whole range of others.

Now dowsing is an exacting exercise. It requires intense concentration and keeps certain muscles constantly under tension. To attempt long sessions of dowsing is therefore unwise. When the dowser becomes fatigued, mistakes start to creep in. When he is confronted with an unexpected result, or one that appears to be bizarre, he should ask himself if it is really valid or if a false result has been obtained because of tiredness. At this point it is advisable to pack up for the day and return fresh to the investigation tomorrow.

That, however, is not the only reason for recommending that dowsing should be undertaken in short sessions. The necessity can be illustrated through the use of some of the simple dowsing techniques described in Chapter 3. Let us suppose that we are establishing the cord length or the Serial Number for iron (see page 29). We place an iron object on a flat surface and by experiment with the long pendulum discover that the cord length for iron is 32in and with the short pendulum that the serial number is 4. The telephone rings and we are called away. In our absence someone clears the table. Half-an-hour elapses before we can resume our experiment. If before we replace the iron object in its original position we test with the long pendulum over the exact spot where it had been resting we shall find we still get the reaction for iron when the cord length is 32in. The short pendulum will still give the Serial Number 4. The iron has, in fact, left behind what seems to be an echo or shadow of itself.

Supposing some other dowser had come along in our absence and tested that surface: he too would have obtained the reactions for iron. But there would have been no iron there. He would have located not the substance itself but evidence that it had been there in the recent past. Unless he was sufficiently experienced to realise what had happened, he would probably think he had made a mistake. Which explains what I meant by suggesting that a useful starting point for our new programme of exploration is an investigation of reputed errors. Were they indeed errors or the failure of a dowser to put the right interpretation on his findings?

In the example given I have assumed that I returned and resumed dowsing within about half-an-hour. The other dowser intervened at an even shorter period after the iron had been removed. Hence I describe the findings as evidence of the presence of iron in the *recent* past. But how recent? How long will the evidence remain? It seems that it will fade gradually, but that the length of time the object has remained in that location has an important bearing on how long its influence persists.

I myself have not dug very deep into this dowsing territory. Once I allowed the head of an iron sledge-hammer to remain in a noted position for three days and then, after its removal, tested the location for traces of it at intervals. I was still obtaining reactions, though faint, four days later but then had to abandon the experiment through being away from home. Here, then, is a sphere in which enthusiastic new dowsers should be able to do a good deal of pioneer work.

One of the most persistent qualities detectable by dowsing techniques is sex. In Chapter 7 a brief reference has been made to the old domestic trick of trying to determine the sex of an unborn child by means of a dowsing pendulum. We have also noted the considerable success recorded by dowsers in sexing hen eggs. Indeed, the chief limitation to this method of separating cockerel chicks from pullet chicks long before hatching is imposed by the stamina of the dowser, who usually cannot work fast enough for long enough to make the technique commercially worthwhile. As he tires he tends to make more and more mistakes.

We have observed that among the cord lengths or rates recorded by the long pendulum are, according to the late T. C. Lethbridge, one for masculinity (24in) and one for femininity (29in). Dowsers are greatly indebted to him for guidance in further research involving both sex and the fourth dimension. I myself have repeated some of his experiments and have confirmed his findings.

Lethbridge was first interested to discover how long a discarded portion of an organism retained its identity or affinity with its parent. He cut off a lock of hair from the head of a living person and placed it in a bottle which was hermetically sealed for a week or two, after which it could with some certainty be pronounced dead. When tested after that interval of time for affinity with the parent body the hair produced a strong reaction. The pendulum oscillated quite violently.

This is one of the experiments I repeated, with the same result. I also tested leaves taken from a living plant and allowed to wilt; also feathers shed by a moulting fowl, and the parings of my own finger-nails. In every instance an affinity with the parent body was quickly established. (Lethbridge points out that there seems to be a connection between the findings of such tests and the age-old witchcraft belief that the possession of a lock of hair, a drop of blood or fingernail parings can give a witch or wizard a certain power over the parent body; hence the eagerness of sorcerers to obtain such a sample. The association is apparent, but I am not sure yet where it leads us.)

Lethbridge tested his hair samples for sex and found that hair from a female head duly responded to a cord length or rate of 29in; hair from a male head responded to a rate of 24in. Wondering how long a dead part of a body would retain evidence of its sex he studied a series of skeletal remains with his pendulum. During experiments made in November 1963, positive evidence of the sex of animal and bird skulls was obtained from skeletons dating from 1919 onwards. The oldest material was thus forty-four years old. The species tested were badger, stoat, weasel, mole, Arctic fox, kestrel, jay, crow, pigeon, puffin, Manx shearwater and heron. In each instance reactions for sex were obtained only from the skull, not from other parts of the skeleton.

He turned his attention to creatures lower in the animal scale and obtained reactions for sex from fishes and crabs. He did also from some old specimens of beetles which he had collected as a boy, forty-five years earlier.

He wondered whether inanimate substances or objects that owed something to their manipulation by humans retained any evidence of the sex of the person who had been involved in shaping them. He tested two pieces of alabaster (which is calcium sulphate); one was just as it had been hewn from the rock, the other had been fashioned into an ornament. The first gave reactions to the following cord lengths or rate of the pendulum: 32in (iron); 26½in (oxygen); 22in (calcium); 7in (sulphur); thus correctly identifying the mineral elements of alabaster. The second gave in addition a reaction to the 24-in rate, indicating a male association. This piece of alabaster had, in fact, been carved by a man. (There was also a reaction to yet another rate — 27in — which is the cord length for the abstract concept of thought, but this will be examined later.)

Lethbridge then examined certain painted portraits he happened to possess. He obtained the expected reactions for the various substances used in paints, plus a reaction to the 24-in rate, which indicates the male principle. One of the portraits was of a lovely lady, but evidently the subject portrayed meant nothing to the pendulum: its reaction was to the sex of the artist, who was in this instance male.

Lethbridge, a trained and experienced archaeologist, next investigated some prehistoric flint implements. One was a flint scraper approximately 3,500 years old. It gave the normal reaction for flint and also indicated associations with thought and with the female principle. He comments that such scrapers were probably used for scraping the fat off skins and that this would be considered a woman's job.

So it seems that sexual characteristics, even through association with inanimate objects, can endure for thousands of years. Obviously this opens an enormous field for investigation and one that has been little explored. I myself have conducted a few experiments on the lines suggested by Lethbridge, and have found nothing to throw doubt on his findings and interpretations, except perhaps in one instance. This was his study of a series of fossil sea-urchins (*Microgaster coranguinum*), which are popularly known as 'shepherd's crowns' or 'fairy loaves'. Out of a collection of 13 of them he obtained a male reaction from 6 specimens, a female reaction from 5, and a reaction for both male and female from 2. Endeavouring to interpret these results, he suggested that the sea-urchins, which lived some 100 million years ago, probably began life without sex, then lived through a period as males, during which they shed their seed. They then had another period as females, during which they laid their eggs. Finally they died. From current knowledge of these creatures the assumption could be correct, but I doubt whether it was warranted by the evidence. The knowledge that such lowly creatures retained evidence of their sex history for 100 million years or so would be interesting and intriguing, but an alternative explanation is possible.

These particular fossils, which can be picked up occasionally on chalk downs, were highly prized by generations of country people, down to very recent times. One or more of them may still be found on many a cottage mantelshelf. Although latterly regarded as mere curiosities, there were lingering memories of their once having a more important significance, connected with magic. The value attached to them a generation or so ago must have been multiplied many times over in more superstitious ages. Many of these fossils must have been handled with respect and even reverence by their possessors, who quite possibly practised as witches or magicians. It could well be that these persons, rather than the sea-urchins themselves, left a sex imprint on the fossils. If so, all that the pendulum is telling us is whether the fossil belonged to a witch or a wizard or to a member of each sex in succession.

One curious though entirely logical subsidiary phenomenon emerged from Lethbridge's study of dowsing and sex. He got an inkling of it when investigating his fossilised sea-urchins but apparently did not follow the lead very far. He found that when he tested a lock of his 'dead' hair against a supposedly female sea-urchin the pendulum oscillated vigorously, denoting an affinity between the two. When, however, he replaced the 'female' sea-urchin by a 'male' specimen the short pendulum switched to gyrations, indicating antipathy. He rightly interpreted this as an indication that in nature male is attracted by female and vice-versa but that two samples of the same sex repel each other. I have tested the theory with a variety of samples and with unvarying results. It does not matter if the samples are from widely different species. Hair from a male, for instance, shows attraction not only to female hair but to a garment worn by a female, a female chick or even a female flower, but is repelled by similar male samples. I do not know what homosexuals will make of this!

Summarising the investigations described in this chapter so far, we cannot escape the conclusion that this sixth sense of ours is able to take account of the fourth dimension. It can be used to convey to our brains evidence not only of length, breadth and height but also of time. The dowsing pendulum can inform us of things past as well as of things present. With its aid we can locate an iron object and also the place where an iron object once laid. Our pendulum will tell us the sex of a long-dead but once animate object such as hair from a human head or the polished skull of a long-deceased animal. It will even reveal the sex of a person involved in making or using an artefact.

One can visualise this ability as being of immense interest to archaeologists. It could also have practical applications in certain police investigations. Logically, too, it might be extended to the future, but of that possibility I can find no evidence at present.

Dowsing can perform yet another function relating to the fourth dimension. It can help to date sites and objects. The technique is simple.

Here as in so many branches of the art, much pioneering work was done by Lethbridge. He discovered that with the long pendulum the cord length of 30in denoted age. A calculation of age could then be made as follows.

The pendulum, set at the correct length, was allowed to oscillate over the site or material, until the oscillations changed to gyrations. The dowser then started to count, continuing until the gyrations switched back to oscillations. That gave the age, and that figure had to be deducted from the present date to date the object. Thus in the year 1982 an object giving a count of 556 could be dated by deduction at AD 1426. As in Lethbridge's experiments it was sometimes difficult to determine exactly when the gyrations began and ended, it was as well to allow a year or two on either side of the date. Even so, it was a very useful exercise, full of promise for dating archaeological items.

When I tried to repeat this experiment I soon discovered the chief snag. Holding a pendulum suspended from a cord 30in long imposes quite a muscular strain after the first ten minutes. To get back a thousand years would take well over half-an-hour, by which time the dowser would have come near to hypnotising himself. Long before then I became giddy, my arm ached and, trying to remember whether I really was on my fourth hundred or only the third, I lost count.

Lethbridge mentioned another problem, which apparently he solved though he does not tell us how. With almost any artefact there are apparently two dates to be discovered, the date of manufacture and the date of loss or deposit. The date indicated by the method described above is the second of these two. Lethbridge prepared comparative tables of both sets of dates but does not reveal his method. However, the dates in each instance are those imposed on an object by humans. The second date is that on which a human last handled it; the first is the date when a human being made it. The object has no intrinsic information to offer about itself; a factory-made object produces no reaction from a long pendulum set to record age.

While this method of dating is intriguing and can be useful for checking, there is an easier method which we shall encounter in a later chapter.

9

Dowsing, Thought and Emotions

When, in the last chapter, we were studying the evidence of sex left in artefacts, as established by dowsing with the long pendulum, we briefly noted that the pendulum also revealed a concept labelled 'thought'.

To investigate this phenomenon we need two dowsers working in harmony. T. C. Lethbridge and his wife Mina worked together in their experiments, and a male/female team may have been the ideal arrangement. Repeating their experiment, I held out my left hand, over which my partner operated a short pendulum. The pendulum in due course began to oscillate. I then started to concentrate hard on some matter which required intense thought; the intricacies of the plot of a book I was writing served very well. As my mind became deeply involved, the pendulum ceased its oscillations and began to gyrate. The experiment was then repeated with the long pendulum, and a cord length or rate of about 27in was established as the correct one for that sort of concentrated thought. It was the same rate as the Lethbridges identified.

Armed with this information Lethbridge discovered the evidence of 'thought' in his alabaster artefact, as described on page 77. He did the same with his fossilised sea-urchins and was puzzled to find a 'thought' rate associated with them. It sent him speculating about whether sea-urchins are able to think, and he came to the conclusion that they were probably capable of sufficient rudimentary thought to enable them to react to certain stimuli, such as changes in the temperature of the surrounding water. That seems doubtful, to say the least, and I prefer the explanation that the 'thought' indicated was that of people who in much more recent times had handled and treasured the fossils. Lethbridge similarly tested a number of other fossil shells but obtained abstract reactions (for thought, sex or any other concept) from only one, an example of *Spondylus spinosa*, which gave a reaction to the thought rate. I would surmise that this was a specimen at one time handled by a person who had devoted considerable thought to it.

Subsequently I tested a wide range of artefacts with a 27-in pendulum. In my study I have a bowl made by a potter working on his own lathe. Suspended over it, the pendulum reacts to the rates of both sex (male) and thought. The potter was evidently concentrating and thinking hard about the bowl as he fashioned it. My brother-in-law fancied that he detected in a piece of wood he picked up the rudimentary likeness of a stoat; getting busy with wood-carving tools, he produced a lovely surrealistic image of the animal. Over this the pendulum gave an enthusiastic reaction for thought. I obtained a reaction for thought over one of my wife's excellent cakes!

But I got no indications at all over a copy of one of my books, which puzzled me at first. I fished out the original manuscript, scribbled in longhand, and dowsed over that. The reaction for thought was clear. Evidently in producing the printed page a mechanical process had intervened. Not only that, but interposed between myseif and the reader were the compositor, the printer, the papermaker and sundry other middlemen. Obviously the physical contact was important. The potter, the wood-carver, the cook, all handled the end products which I had been studying, but I never handled the actual book. It contained my thoughts, coded in the form of printed words, but with the pendulum that did not count. There were too many intermediaries.

We are perhaps moving ahead too fast. With the testing of all these artefacts we are again introducing the fourth dimension. In all of them we are exploring not the present existence of thought but the evidence of thought that has occurred in the past (whether recent or distant seems to make no difference) and has left its imprint. In the initial experiment to determine the rate or cord-length for thought, on the other hand, we were dealing with contemporary thought, present at that moment, which the pendulum was able to detect.

Now that corresponds with the discoveries about thought made by Cleve Backster in his New York laboratories in 1966. A specialist in lie-detection apparatus, Backster in an idle moment attached the electrodes of one of his lie-detectors to the leaf of a dracaena, an ornamental pot-plant in his office. The way in which lie-detectors work is by recording on a graph the reactions of the subject under test (normally a human being) to various stimuli featuring thought and emotion. Sometimes it is expedient to introduce a threat. Backster decided he would do so with his dracaena plant: he resolved to burn the leaf to which the electrodes were attached. Immediately he made this decision and before he had time to act upon it the recording needle of the graph gave a dramatic leap.

Intrigued, Backster conducted a comprehensive series of tests on a variety of plants. Because of his privileged position as the leading lie-detector examiner in the USA he was able to do so under laboratory conditions in a number of locations throughout the country. His experiments convincingly demonstrated that plants react positively to thought.

His subsequent programme of investigation was too detailed and exhaustive to be recounted here, but it revealed that plants are not only sensitive to thought but are apparently more sensitive to it than to actual physical stimuli. Thus, a pot plant reacted to a decision of a spider to scuttle away to a hiding-place on the approach of a human being at the very moment of decision and a fraction of a second before the spider actually moved. Backster, who personally attended to the needs of his plants and so established an affinity with them, found that they reacted to his thoughts and emotions when he left the room and went walking in the street. Graphs produced by electrodes fastened to their leaves faithfully recorded his mental adventures when he was absent.

Arising largely from his experiments, the study of the reaction of plants to human thoughts and emotions has been proceeding rapidly and will be referred to again later. Here it is sufficient to say that thought as a factor which can produce physical effects in the discernible world has been thoroughly established, and dowsing techniques can detect it.

Thought is based largely on memory. When thinking hard

about any subject we can hardly escape introducing memories we have associated with it. Past experiences guide our present reasoning and decisions. Therefore it is hardly surprising that the Lethbridges found it impossible to separate thought from memory by dowsing. The long pendulum rate they established was the same for both, namely 27in.

They did, however, determine rates or cord lengths for certain other abstract concepts. All living things, they discovered, gave a reaction to a 20-in cord length; all dead ones to a 40-in cord. The 20-in rate they therefore term the life-force; the 40-in rate indicated either sleep or death (for a dormant creature, such as a hibernating animal, also gave a reaction to the 40-in cord).

They tested for the emotion *anger*. This can be done by holding the pendulum over the left hand, allowing it to oscillate and then thinking of something that makes you really angry. Then lower the pendulum till it switches from oscillation to gyration and measure the cord-length at that point. That is the rate for anger. The Lethbridges arrived at 40in, as for sleep and death. I myself have had little success with this experiment, probably because I cannot in cold blood work up a proper degree of anger.

Having determined the 40-in rate for anger, the Lethbridges used it to test a collection of sling-stones from an Iron Age fortress at Wandlebury, near Cambridge (where T. C. Lethbridge had excavated in his capacity of Director of Excavations of the Cambridge Antiquarian Society). Seven out of the 110 stones gave a reaction at the 40-in rate. Later they examined another collection found during excavation of Iron Age camps at Pilsdon Pen and Blackbury Camp, in Dorset. Here many of the pebbles reacted at the 40-in rate. The sling-stones from these two latter sites may have been last used when Vespasian stormed the citadels in the course of his campaign in the West Country in AD47 and 48, though they may have been thrown in inter-tribal wars at an earlier date. It is logical to conclude that they were thrown in the heat of battle by combatants who were in the throes of considerable emotion. The Lethbridges were convinced that their findings were evidence of anger, though I suppose they might equally well have indicated death. The intriguing point, though, is that for 2,000 years or more the stones retained evidence of the emotions of the men who last handled them.

We are thus led to a consideration of the phenomena of ghosts. If a human being, particularly one in the grip of strong emotions, can leave behind him evidence detectable by dowsing apparatus, there may be certain conditions under which his or her existence may be revealed to other senses. Ghosts are usually associated with emotions such as fear, despair, anger, love and remorse. We hear of apparitions wringing their hands in desperation and of feelings of depression or terror attacking sensitive people in certain environments. We also hear of houses that seem filled with benign influences, emanating, it is said, from the happiness of people who once lived there. All these things should be capable of being investigated by a dowser.

I myself have never been privileged to investigate a place alleged to be haunted but can suggest a method of approach for a dowser. He should establish what are for him the rates for anger, love, fear and other emotions and then explore the environment with long pendulums with cords of the appropriate lengths. He should be able to discover the sex of the apparition and the prevalent emotion involved. By the method already described he ought to be able to put a date to the events with which the ghost is concerned. He might also be able to learn the age of the person whose personality has left traces in the place — for, according to Lethbridge, a 10-in rate indicates youth, a 30-in rate age.

In Chapter 4 we took note of the aura which surrounds the human body. Conditions of extreme stress could conceivably allow this aura to impose on its environment a kind of photographic image or shadow which might linger for long periods after the event. Sensitive people might conceivably become aware of its presence, to some degree, by the senses of sight and feeling as well as by the mysterious sixth sense of which the dowsing rod and pendulum are the organs.

There is one further development in this increasingly abstruse aspect of dowsing. Lethbridge considered that his dowsing experiments had provided evidence of life after death!

Readers will already have noted that the most important

rates concerning abstract matters, as recorded by the long pendulum, occur in multiples of ten. Thus 10 itself indicates light, youth and love; 20 is the rate for life and electricity; 30 is for age and also for sound; 40 is the ultimate and indicates anger, sleep and death. If these are arranged in diagrammatic form as points on a circle, they coincide with the cardinal divisions. Place them so that 40 marks the North pole. Then, moving clockwise, 10 will represent East, 20 South, and 30 West. Between these cardinal points we can fit in the other rates we have established, such as 12 for carbon, 26½ for oxygen or water, and so on, and those for abstract ideas such as the male and female principle.

Lethbridge prepared such a diagram. On it he marked the rates for each item according to length of cord and direction and found he had drawn a spiral. Sulphur, for instance, with a rate of seven was seven units from the starting point, in a direction seven-tenths of the sector between North and East. Silica, with a rate of 14, was four points south of the line from centre to East. The rate for life and electricity, 20, lay due south of the centre, at a distance of 20 units. And so on until the 40-in rate for death and sleep was reached.

But the spiral did not end there. Projected further, the sequence was repeated, with the addition of 40 to each item. Thus at that level a rate or cord length of 47 gave the reaction for sulphur; that of 54 for silica; that of 60 the reaction for life and electricity. The spiral went even farther, to 80, to 100 and indeed perhaps to infinity. Lethbridge tested it as far as he was able, by using the well of a staircase to accommodate his pendulum. (Remember that a rate of 54 is found by a pendulum with a cord length of 54in, so a lot of vertical space is needed to pursue this investigation.) He could see no logical reason for the spiral ever ending.

Lethbridge interpreted his findings as indicating a continuation of life after death. He quoted Buddhist and Hindu beliefs in a long sequence of lives on earth, though he considered the pendulum was providing evidence of life on other planes. For while many things were the same on the second coil of the spiral as on the first, some were different. One of the most important was *Time*.

In his experiments with subjects up to the rate of 40in he

was unable to fix a rate for time. This, he suggested, was because time is always moving. On the second spiral, however, he was able to establish a rate for time. It was 60in, the same as for life. He took this to indicate that time on that plane is static. A person living there would have infinite time at his disposal. Winston Churchill would have no difficulty in achieving his professed ambition of spending the first few million years of eternity in learning how to paint.

It all sounds logical and in accordance with many ideas about an after-life in the teaching of several religions. Just what value, however, one should place on the evidence of the pendulum in these metaphysical matters the reader must decide for himself. Not having a three-storey house with a deep staircase-well I have been unable to repeat Lethbridge's experiment!

10
How Does Dowsing Work?

My approach to the subject of dowsing has, in the first nine chapters of this book, been essentially practical. Starting with the simple dowsing technique of finding underground water, which I myself can do and which hundreds of thousands of other people can do, once they know how, we have progressed to more advanced studies: dowsing for minerals or for concealed objects, to establish affinities, to diagnose disease and even to investigate abstract phenomena. Throughout the study I have stuck to my resolve to present only such information as can be readily obtained by other dowsers or would-be dowsers, employing the simplest apparatus. The fact that I have used only the divining rod and the long and short pendulums may seem a weakness to those who would prefer to be introduced to more sophisticated methods, but this book is for beginners who do not have access to such aids (although many do exist and more are being developed).

Wherever possible I have described experiments and investigations which I myself have made, but the subject is so vast that already it could occupy several lifetimes and it is still rapidly expanding. Beyond my own studies, therefore, I have quoted the experiments and experiences of other dowsers, being careful always to present the facts without bothering much about theory. My attitude has been: this is how it is done, these are the results obtained; now go and test them for yourself and explain them how you will.

Nevertheless, at this juncture it may be helpful to look at some of the theories and explanations that have been advanced to account for the phenomena observed. That a dowser holding a supple twig or a pendulum can locate underground streams and hidden objects and obtain a great deal of other information does seem somewhat nonsensical. The ridicule sometimes poured upon dowsing by scientists of various disciplines is not to be wondered at. One thing that is certain, however, is that the dowser is not cheating. Nor is he deceiving himself. I remember my surprise and disbelief when I first learned that I could dowse, when I first felt the rod twisting uncontrollably in my grasp, and I am used to similar incredulous reactions from those whom I introduce to the art. That dowsing reveals information which can be proved to be accurate is an incontrovertible fact. Those scientists still inclined to criticise would be better occupied investigating the facts and seeking to explain them than trying to ignore them.

The best approach to a theoretical study of dowsing is to regard it as a sixth sense. How does one describe or explain a sense, especially to a person who does not possess it? H. G. Wells developed the theme in his novel *The Country of the Blind*. 'In the country of the blind the one-eyed man is king', claimed an ancient proverb, but Wells showed that it would not be so. The citizens of the Country of the Blind had over many generations achieved what was to them a satisfactory explanation of their environment, as revealed by their four senses. They had not made a bad job of it, but in some respects they were hopelessly wrong. Heaven, they believed, was a realm not far above their heads, for could they not hear the angels singing? The angels were birds, creatures of which they had no conception. But when the hero, blessed with full sight, tried to correct their ideas he was met by unmitigated hostility. They would not admit there was another sense which they did not possess. Therefore anything allegedly revealed by that sense was just a lie or hallucination.

We see because we have organs — eyes — which can utilise light waves. Those of us who can see take sight for granted, but few of us could explain just how our eyes work. Could you explain to a blind man how your eyes enable you to estimate distance? Could you describe colour? Or perspective? Our eyes enable us to see the world as it is — or so we are inclined to think. But they have limitations. They cannot see ultra-violet or infra-red waves in the spectrum. We are presented with two

90

flowers, both apparently white. When subjected to ultra-violet light, one glows and the other does not. Ultra-violet light reveals in the first flower a colour which we cannot see; we cannot imagine what it looks like. If we could see it, our impression of the world around us would change dramatically. Just as red and blue combine to make purple, and blue and yellow to make green, so doubtless the ultra-violet colour combines with other primary colours to make new ones we cannot visualise. Moths, which share our world, can see ultra-violet light. The environment familiar to us must appear very different to them.

There is in the universe an infinity of waves, rays, force currents, call them what you will. Dowsing can evidently pick up some of them. T. C. Lethbridge, who has been frequently quoted in the preceding chapters, comments that if the fields of force revealed as 'cones' in his investigations were visible they would seem like a forest of tapering tentacles, gently swaying as they reached towards the sky. Dowsing has demonstrated that each of us is surrounded by an aura, and recently developed techniques, notably Kirlian photography, have made it to some extent visible. Living subjects photographed by this process are shown to possess an aura glowing and flashing with sparkling light.

Conventional theories of dowsing speak of 'rays' to which the dowser, through his rod or pendulum, is susceptible. Early engravings of dowsing depict the dowser at work with his forked twig over ground from which emanations from subterranean water are rising like vapour. To repeat a quotation already given, Lyall Watson, in his book *Supernature*, says that 'Water, by the action of friction between itself and the soil, creates a field which could have electro-magnetic qualities.' Whether or not friction is responsible, it has been scientifically established that over zones where the presence of subterranean water has been demonstrated, considerable ionisation of the air occurs. The phenomenon, which has been described as telluric radiation, is related to radioactivity. Lead sheets placed over the zones will cut off the emissions, and apparatus related to the Geiger counter has been devised to measure them.

It is probably no coincidence that the practical application of dowsing should begin with water. Water is a mysterious substance. Unlike almost all others, it is denser as a liquid than as a solid, which is why ice floats. Were it not for that anomaly, ice would sink to the bottom of the oceans and remain there, making the earth uninhabitable. Although its composition is simple — two atoms of hydrogen and one of oxygen — the water molecule has a curious pattern. The two hydrogen atoms are held on one side of the oxygen, producing a lop-sided entity. The oxygen side of the atom develops a negative charge, while the hydrogen side becomes positively charged. The molecule thus becomes a kind of magnet.

Water is an almost universal solvent. Even falling rain, which is one of the purest forms of water, dissolves and absorbs other gases in the atmosphere. In the soil, in lakes and rivers and in the sea it is incessantly dissolving other substances with which it comes into contact. This happens because the water molecule is more stable and more resistant to disruption than many of the other molecules it encounters. It forces apart the ions which form these soluble substances and which are held together by an electrical force, known as an ionic bond. The reaction of water molecules on the molecules which are being thus dissolved produces or releases electricity.

Why does the air above a subterranean water source contain an excess of ions? Presumably they are being shed by substances in the process of dissolution by the water. Or perhaps by the water itself, as an electric or electro-magnetic current passes through it. A prodigious series of experiments carried out in Italy and Belgium in the 1950s showed that chemical reactions occurring in water were related to sunspot activity and to changes in the earth's magnetic field. Our bodies are composed 65 per cent of water. Is there an affinity between what is happening in our bodies and what is happening to the water in the ground beneath our feet?

What of the so-called 'black springs', which affect the health of those living above them? Is it the excess of ions released by the chemical reaction of water with other substances which is injurious to health? What can be claimed with reasonable safety is that, whatever the nature of the emissions from underground streams, they are detectable by dowsers, even with primitive instruments.

The book *Practical Dowsing*, a symposium edited by Colonel A. H. Bell, founder and first President of the British Society of Dowsers, and published in 1965, contains a contribution by a dowser, A. D. Manning, on 'The Neutralization of Harmful Rays'. Manning claims that 'for the past twenty years or so I have been engaged in this type of work, having protected some 2,000 homes throughout the United Kingdom'. He bases his activities on the belief (for which, we have seen, there is a great deal of evidence) that certain underground streams adversely affect the health of persons and animals living above them, and he undertakes to counteract their effects.

His method is to determine, by dowsing techniques, the course of the stream and the direction in which the water is moving. In a convenient spot on the line of each stream, upstream from the building in question, he digs a hole about 12in square and 6in deep and in it inserts his apparatus, which consists of a wooden core with copper wire tightly coiled around it. Attached, like horns, to the top end of the core are two steel rods, $\frac{5}{8}$in in diameter around which more copper wire is wound. They are linked at their positive ends, which are also in contact with the core, while the negative ends remain about 12in apart. It is claimed that the emanations from the underground water are by this means interrupted, with the result that the health of the subjects living above the water is greatly improved. The author gives several instances of cures effected, and his total of over 2,000 cases is impressive. It looks as though the device is trapping an electric or electromagnetic current; maybe a method could be devised for measuring or even utilising the power thus collected.

Locating underground water is only the beginning of dowsing. Quite early in our investigations we moved on to the location of minerals, compound substances and objects and to the determination of affinities, all of which can be studied by means of the rod and pendulum. Are we then to claim that all substances are emitting radiation of some kind? It would seem so. Nor is that surprising or illogical. Consider the enormous range of objects of which we become aware through our sense of sight, which operates by being susceptible to light waves. Why should our sixth sense be less efficient than our sense of sight?

All the evidence so far encountered points in the same direction. A theory of radiation would account for cones and auras, for affinities and repulsions, as well as the straightforward locating of concealed objects. There is even a bit of additional evidence to be found in the behaviour of the pendulum when investigating affinities. When two objects or substances under investigation were compatible the pendulum oscillated smoothly, but when an incompatible item was introduced the oscillation changed to gyration. Consider what seems to have happened. The pendulum, swinging easily to and fro, has encountered an obstruction. It bounces back, turns, advances again, is again repulsed and so settles down to a circular or gyratory movement. It is the sort of reaction that could be expected if the obstruction were visible. In this instance it is invisible, but real for all that.

Chapter 8 provides evidence of the durability of the radiation involved, whatever it may be. In some instances it seems to defy time and so is able to offer information of considerable value to archaeologists. Here again, when studying archaeological remains, we rely on the evidence of our eyes, so why not on the evidence of our sixth sense? And now, having advanced and examined a theory which appears to account for every phenomenon we have so far observed, we move on, in Chapter 12, to a further aspect of the subject where it seems quite inadequate!

11

'Track Lines' and Megaliths

This is an anomalous chapter. I am not sure where it fits into the broad pattern of dowsing. So far we have taken logical steps from the simple location of underground water to the abstract and metaphysical matters dealt with in the last chapter. What we are now going to consider seems to me a diversion, and yet those who regard it as one of the most important aspects of dowsing may not be exaggerating.

It was pioneered in the mid-twentieth century by Guy Underwood, whose book *The Pattern of the Past* is now regarded as a minor classic. Underwood, an archaeologist who died at the age of eighty-one in 1966, became convinced that ancient sites, particularly standing stones and prehistoric stone structures, were positioned over underground water sources or what he termed 'blind springs'.

He states that in addition to water lines there are other types of subterranean phenomena detectable by dowsers. To two of them he gives the name 'track lines' and 'aquastats'. In a contribution to the *Journal of the British Society of Dowsers* he wrote: 'It seems a pity that so much emphasis has been placed on water in connection with dowsing. The fact that it is possible to find water supplies by dowsing is an isolated and, possibly, minor phenomenon of a far more important physical fact — the existence of a geophysical force so far not identified.'

He points out that the term 'underground streams' is generally a misnomer. Only rarely does subterranean water occur in the form of free-flowing streams. He explains: 'The facts are that underground water, usually at considerable depth and pressure, forces itself through beds of gravel or sand, or narrow fissures in the rock, trying to find an outlet where its pressure can be relieved.'

The contention apparently is that what the dowser finds is evidence of the fissures, and the fact that most of them are filled with water is incidental. Underwood separates dowsers, or more particularly water diviners, into two main classes, which he calls respectively positive and negative dowsers. *Negative dowsers* are those who, when approaching an underground stream, find the pointer of their forked twig lifting at some distance from the centre of the stream, as described earlier. I, like most dowsers, am a negative dowser. A *positive dowser*, a much rarer creature, gets no reaction at all from his rod until he is right over the spring, when the reaction is usuallly very strong indeed. Positive dowsers are the ones who can detect all Underwood's primary lines, which he termed 'geodetic' lines. He gives the following instructions for finding these phenomena.

For detecting a *water-line* (which is the sort that ordinary or negative dowsers normally find), grasp the forked rod very firmly with the left hand and lightly with the right; for detecting a *track-line*, grasp the rod very firmly with the right hand and lightly with the left; for detecting an *aquastat*, grasp the rod as for discovering a track-line but not so tightly.

Later he invented his own dowsing device, the 'geodetic rod', a somewhat complicated piece of apparatus which most dowsers seem to find very awkward to use, though Underwood managed it easily enough and obtained remarkably detailed results with it.

His *track-lines* he so named because on the surface they were usually marked by the course of some ancient track or field boundary. He afterwards altered the name to '*geostats*'.

His *aquastats* resemble, according to the testimony of dowsing instruments, water-lines but 'run continuously without breaks . . . They join with other crossing aquastats and form a continuous network over the whole country.'

Water-lines, according to Underwood, are composed of 'three parallel influence lines, of which the centre one is always considerably stronger than the outside influences'. This apparently is another way of describing the normal method for locating underground water, as given in Chapter 1.

Track-lines differ from water-lines in that 'they are always composed of three sets of three parallel influence lines'. That makes nine lines in all, and for the sensitive dowser the rod gives a definite kick as each line is crossed. The current or influence or whatever it is which affects the rod is weaker than with water-lines.

Aquastats may be discovered by both negative and positive dowsers. They consist of three parallel lines, as with water-lines from 3 to 60ft apart. The lines themselves have breadth, given by Underwood as 2 or 3ft.

In the 1930s French researchers recorded that many standing stones (megaliths) stood where two or more dowsing lines intersected. Their work was taken up by two British dowsers, Captain F. L. M. Boothby and R. Allender Smith, who found that barrows, sacred stones and similar prehistoric features were situated above 'knots' of converging lines. Smith called these knots 'blind springs', a term which Underwood readily adopted. His books are lavishly illustrated with diagrams showing prehistoric sites marked by a labyrinth of wavering lines. His explanatory drawings showing the parallel lines forming spirals, reticulations, whorls, 'reversed circles', arcs and other patterns take a lot of understanding.

Underwood's contention is that most prehistoric sites are located on blind springs. He mentions Stonehenge, Avebury, Stanton Drew and numerous other megalithic structures as examples and states that tumuli in general are so sited, thus agreeing with the findings of Boothby and Smith and of the Frenchmen, Merle and Diot. He further maintains that most of the great medieval cathedrals were similarly aligned to geodetic lines. With regard to cathedrals and churches he goes into considerable detail, claiming to trace geodetic lines in the sitings of altars, chancels, fonts, stoups, spirit bowls and indeed virtually every architectural feature. He submits a detailed study of Winchester, Salisbury and Chichester cathedrals and of Westminster Abbey, his diagrams showing a labyrinth of water-lines and aquastats. In Chichester cathedral, he points out, there is hardly a straight line or a true rectangle anywhere, which in view of the accuracy and impressive achievements of medieval builders can hardly have been accidental. The explanation, he declares, is that all the lines follow the course of geodetic lines, which he has checked with his dowsing apparatus. He finds similar geodetic lines coinciding with such landscape features as gateways, ponds, fords, churchyard walls and traditional places of execution.

Reverting to prehistoric sites, he conducts a very detailed survey of Stonehenge, the White Horse of Uffington and the Cerne Abbas Giant. At Stonehenge he analyses the individual stones. The so-called Slaughter Stone, for instance, is not only 'outlined precisely by aquastats' but 'marks a cluster of blind springs or nodes, the spiral terminals of which are marked by basins, of which there are seventeen'. His geodetic survey of the Cerne Abbas Giant similarly shows a maze of meandering lines and spirals, every detail of the gigantic hill figure being marked by a geodetic line.

What are we to make of all this? As a secondary criticism, Underwood does not help his case by certain inaccuracies in the supporting evidence. For instance, he quotes the fact that 'some churches are half a mile or more from the villages they serve' as evidence of some unexplained and mysterious factor in their siting. He ignores generally accepted explanation that in the course of centuries the village, which was once clustered around the church, has moved away from it. He quotes the size of certain village churches, pointing out that they are often 'utterly disproportionate to past and present congregations'. That splendid old rustic politician, William Cobbett, touring the country in 1826, quoted the same fact as evidence that the villages had once been much more populous. The true explanation is that the churches in question were not built primarily for the use of local congregations but to the glory of God and, more particularly, to reflect the wealth, munificence and piety of the builder. In other words, many were 'fire escapes', constructed for the purpose of helping their builder to escape hell fire.

He rejects the explanation that many churchyards are raised several feet above the adjoining land in order to accommodate centuries of burials, and calculates how many corpses would be needed to raise the level of the soil a few inches. Nevertheless it is known that the monks of Glastonbury Abbey, to give one instance, deliberately raised the level of the burial ground when it became full, so that another layer of corpses could be interred above the existing one, and no doubt the same thing happened in other places.

These, however, are secondary matters. What intrigues me is how Underwood managed to achieve such marvellous accuracy as he claims. How did he follow the courses of seventeen blind springs, with associated whorls and spirals and numerous other geodetic lines, under a single stone at Stonehenge, even though it is 21ft long? How was he able to dowse so accurately on the steep hillsides on which the Cerne Abbas Giant and the Uffington White Horse are carved? He is so enthusiastic about his discoveries and theories that he neglects to give details of some of the preliminary steps. One gathers, too, that the criticism he received, even from fellow dowsers, tended to make him dogmatic.

Certain intriguing similarities with other aspects of dowsing we have been discussing suggest themselves. The knots and spirals of Underwood's blind springs seem to have an affinity with the spiral traced by Lethbridge. And they are very similar, too, to the mazes, cut on turf or marked by stones, which are still found on numerous medieval and prehistoric sites. Archaeologists believe them to have been constructed for ritual dances connected with religious observances. The earlier ones may well have had an association with fertility. Many are connected with prehistoric sites such as Celtic field boundaries and hill forts. Of similar design and equally suggestive are the 'cup-and-ring' markings, which are patterns, carved on stone, of small concentric circles often joined by wavy lines. Reams of paper have been devoted to expounding tentative explanations, but they still remain a mystery. Both mazes and 'cup-and-ring' markings have an almost universal distribution, being found in Europe, North America, Africa, Asia and even Polynesia. Readers who are interested in this fascinating branch of dowsing will probably want to read Underwood's book and investigate some of his claims for themselves.

It has already been suggested that the force to which dowsers react is connected with, or similar to, electromagnetism. In his book *Earth Magic*, Francis Hitching suggests that certain stones tend to magnify the power of this force, much as a magnifying lens enhances the impact of light or hearing devices amplify sound. 'The molecular structure of quartz is spiral,' he states, 'and may be lefthanded or righthanded, just as on the carved decorations at Newgrange. It is also piezo-electric; that is, it expands slightly if given a slight charge of electricity. If placed under pressure — as it would be if charged while inside another stone — alternate edges of its prism give off positive and negative voltages on what can reach a dramatic scale; a force of 1,000 pounds applied on each face of a half-inch crystal creates 25,000 volts.' There must be many quartz crystals in ancient rocks which are subjected to far greater pressures. Maybe, Hitching suggests, they can react similarly to forces other than electricity, and particularly to the force to which dowsers are sensitive.

The phenomenon is not unconnected with the attempt at present in progress to utilise the heat generated by masses of quartz under pressure. Bores are being sunk in thick granite strata in Cornwall to depths at which the heat will be sufficient to raise water forced into the bores to high temperatures, thus providing a valuable new source of energy.

Folklore and traditions are full of stories ascribing supernatural properties to stones, particularly monoliths, standing upright and alone. Some of these are said to turn around when the cock crows; some walk round fields or go down to the river to drink at specified bewitching hours; some are the petrified figures of revellers caught dancing on a Sunday; some are fossilised witches. Many are associated with healing and are alleged to have healing powers. Writing of Stonehenge in the thirteenth century Geoffrey of Monmouth, quoting ancient tradition, asserts: 'In these stones is a mystery . . . and a healing virtue against many ailments . . . Not a stone is there that lacketh in virtue of witchcraft.' As late as the eighteenth century visitors to Stonehenge were in the habit of taking scrapings of the stones in the belief that they would cure a wide range of diseases.

Newgrange, in county Meath, Ireland, mentioned above, is an outstanding example of a prehistoric passage grave, dating probably from about 2500 BC. Its massive stones are decorated with intricate carvings featuring spirals, cup-and-ring markings, lozenges and triangles. Some fine specimens of cup-

and-ring markings, dating from the Bronze Age, may be seen on a stone slab at Roughting Linn, in Northumberland, and similar carvings are not uncommon in Yorkshire and other northern counties. They resemble the ground plan of Stonehenge, Avebury and many other stone circles, and Avebury even has the emerging wavy line of the carvings, here represented by the Kennet Avenue, leading to the Sanctuary on Overton Hill. A motif so often repeated must have had some significance, but we are so far removed from its makers that we can hardly understand their modes of thought.

Once when visiting a tribe of Indians, descended from the Maya, in Central America I was out at sea in a dug-out canoe when we met a big turtle travelling urgently north-westwards. It was on its annual migration to the turtle breeding-grounds off Nicaragua. My two Indian companions did their best to describe to this ignorant European the significance of its journey. 'It is going', they said, 'to pay homage to the King of the Turtles. The King of the Turtles is a great stone which looks like a turtle. And although it is a stone, yet that stone lives!' Here were primitive people, illiterate and little touched by the modern world, who retained an instinctive awareness of properties of the natural world of which we had little knowledge. And apparently they held the same beliefs about certain big stones as did our Neolithic and Bronze Age ancestors.

Francis Hitching suggests that prehistoric man, endowed with a sense which in most of us has become atrophied, was able to discern the force within the stones. First he would feel or sense the active force within the stone. Then he would discover that the force was enhanced if the stones were sited on dowsing or radiation lines, of which he was also aware. Once that was recognised, there would be a powerful incentive to move great stones to favourable sites, and the observable coincidence of megaliths and dowsing lines would be explained.

As for the spiral motif, certain parallels may or may not have significance. The DNA molecule, recently discovered, which is the basis of all life, is formed of a double spiral. Whirlpools, the Atlantic depressions which bring rain, cyclonic storms and the galaxies of the universe, are likewise spirals. And the serpent of early serpent-worshipping religions, which were distributed almost world-wide, is often depicted in spiral form, like a coiled cobra.

A recent theory that upsets the orthodox concept of the hydrological cycle deserves a mention here. The long-accepted idea has been that all water originates in the oceans, from which water vapour ascends into the atmosphere to form clouds. Air currents carry the clouds over land, where the water is precipitated in the form of rain, hail or snow. From the land much of it is returned to the sea by way of streams and rivers, but some first passes through the systems of innumerable plants and animals. A residue seeps into the earth, there to collect in reservoirs deep in the rock, which can be tapped by bores and wells.

Investigators, especially those connected with mining, have long been puzzled by the occurrence of water in primary rocks, quite often at high altitudes where natural drainage seems to be inadequate to account for it. In the present century a German mining engineer now resident in the USA, Stephan Riess, has explained the phenomenon by the theory that deep in such rocks oxygen and hydrogen atoms, subjected to electrochemical forces, combine to form new water which has never been part of an ocean. Riess, in a long career involving work in a number of countries (he was responsible for finding the water which supplies the Israeli port of Eilat, on the Red Sea), has accumulated an impressive dossier of achievements based on his theory. It looks as though it is water of this type, lurking in rock fissures, which is frequently found by dowsers.

12

Dowsing from Maps
and Photographs

The branch of dowsing to which we now turn is dowsing from a distance, by means of maps and photographs. Readers whose credulity already feels strained may well exclaim, 'This is nonsense!' That was my initial reaction when I was introduced to it. The only retort that can be made is to refer to results.

Let me describe my first venture into map-dowsing. I started with a locality I knew well, my own house and its environs, and checked that the underground streams I knew, from previous explorations with the dowsing rod, existed. I obtained a 6-in Ordnance Survey map of the area and laid it flat on the table. Some authorities said that it should be placed so that North on the map coincided with true North, so that is what I did, though subsequent experiences tell me it is not really important. In my left hand I took a pointer, one of those wooden meat-skewers already mentioned. Between thumb and forefinger of my right hand I held a short pendulum, not over the map but over the bare table to one side of it. I placed the tip of the pointer on the map, at a point near the house, and moved it slowly towards what I already knew to be the line of an underground stream. When it reached that line the pendulum, which had been gently oscillating, began to gyrate.

I tried approaching the line of the subterranean water from other directions and obtained the same response. I turned my attention to other springs that my dowsing-rod had located in the past. In every instance when I reached their part of the map the pendulum gyrated.

So far, so good. The recommended system was working. Of course, the immediate objection that occurred to me was that, as I already knew where the streams were, my subconcious mind was affecting the pendulum. Undoubtedly that was a valid criticism. So I tried map-dowsing in other areas where I did not know the location of underground streams and again obtained reactions which looked reasonable. But here the snag was that I had no means of testing their accuracy.

Then I was asked to try to locate a source of water on a large farm in southern Portugal which was suffering from drought. The owners provided a fairly large map of the farm — not large enough, unfortunately, to enable me to pinpoint a location to within a few yards, but large enough to allow an indication of any vicinity in which water was to be found.

Having laid the map flat on the table I moved the short pendulum gently over it, experimenting. Over certain sections of it the pendulum began to gyrate, and these I concentrated on. I now moved the pointer over the map while suspending the pendulum over the bare table. I started with the tip of the pointer on the edge of one of the areas suggested by my preliminary survey and moved it slowly around. Presently the pendulum in my other hand began to gyrate. I continued to move the pointer, now very slowly, until the pendulum had attained its maximum gyration, and I marked the place on the map.

I approached the area from other directions and eventually found I had a sinuous line of crosses on the map. These I took to mark the course of an underground stream. I located several others on the map, but two seemed to have particular promise. They converged. I recommended to the owners that the point where they met seemed the most promising spot to sink a bore, and so it proved. A good supply of water was found there.

The experience boosted my confidence considerably. I did not, however, have sufficient evidence to venture a prediction of depth or quantity. To determine quantity, one uses the same technique as for dowsing on the spot, but to achieve any worthwhile results with the pendulum and a map one needs a map on a large scale. One method of determining the depth at which the water is to be found is to count aloud, as described on page 24. At a certain number the pendulum ceases to oscillate and starts to gyrate, and that number indicates depth. This business of counting aloud seems nonsensical and diffident dowsers do so with some embarrassment; once again all we can say is that it does seem to work.

Incidentally, the method described for map-dowsing may also be employed to find subterranean water from an aerial photograph.

Theoretically, such feats as these ought to be impossible. Theories based on radiation or electromagnetic currents are of no help. In Chapter 8 I describe how T. C. Lethbridge found that although he could obtain reactions for sex, thought and other abstract notions by using the long pendulum over paintings and artefacts, he could get no such results from photographs or books. Although a book is the reproduction of the author's thoughts, there is no physical contact between it and the author. It is a mechanically reproduced copy of what is, in essence, a code that enables us to follow what the author wishes to say. A book may tell the reader quite a lot about an author, but it tells the dowsing rod or pendulum nothing. A map or a photograph should therefore convey to the dowser no relevant information at all.

Yet it does. The incident from my own experience, described above, is no isolated example. Experienced dowsers are performing similar feats every day of the year — and some are being paid good money for their services. As long ago as 1933 the Government of Alberta was paying substantial sums to a dowser for successfully locating water by map-dowsing. Around the same period the neighbouring province of British Columbia employed a professional dowser who conducted preliminary explorations of remote areas by map-dowsing. In Russia the technique is widely accepted and used. The Czechoslovak army is said to have a corps of dowsers. The US Marines employed dowsing extensively to locate enemy tunnels, caches and ambushes in the Vietnam war. Many American oil companies employ dowsers to find new reserves of oil.

Further details of achievements in this field are found in Chapter 14. They add up to an impressive testimony that map-dowsing is a valid technique that can produce verifiable results.

How can the dowser know that it is water which he is finding by his explorations on the map? Surely the pendulum indicates the presence of substances other than water? It does indeed, and the objection is a valid one. As water is the substance which most commonly produces a dowsing reaction, it is the one which a dowser is most likely to find, but there are several methods of making sure. One is by the use of the long pendulum, as described on page 29. Map-dowsers, of course, commonly use the short pendulum (with a cord of from 3 to 8in). The long pendulum has a cord of some 40in, and for most dowsers the length of cord or rate for locating water is 26½in. So when one explores a map with a cord of that length, the gyrations of the pendulum will indicate the presence of water. A natural drawback to the use of the long pendulum for map-dowsing is, of course, that it is very tiring.

A second method is to use a sample. The approved procedure is to hold a sample of whatever one wishes to locate against the rod or the cord of the pendulum. But be sure that it *is* a genuine sample. There should be no difficulty with minerals or plants or even human beings, but a picture or a representation of the object can be misleading. Let us suppose you are asked to indicate the whereabouts of a lost dog. Some combings of the dog's coat will be a useful sample, but a photograph of the dog will not.

In my early dowsing days I myself fell foul of that snare. At the time the disappearance of a child was attracting a good deal of attention in the Press, and I felt that a proficient dowser ought to be able to help. So from a newspaper I cut out a photograph of the child to use as a sample, and with that held in my hand against the cord of a short pendulum I proceeded to map-dowse. I worked first of all on an atlas map of England, from which I obtained an indication that what I sought was in the Midlands. On a map with a much larger scale I narrowed down the search further. Eventually I was able to point to a street in a certain Midland city which, according to my pendulum, held the key to the mystery. It happened to be a city where I had a contact so I asked him to investigate. His somewhat devastating reply showed me where I had gone wrong. What I had discovered was a paper mill, probably the source of the paper on which the picture had been printed!

In determining what substance the pendulum is reacting to we can also use Serial Numbers or the Mager Rosette (see page 31). Basically, both methods are variations on samples.

A final method is to dispense entirely with samples and to rely on a mental approach. First banish from your mind all you have learnt about the behaviour of the pendulum (the *short* pendulum is the one which you will be using). Relax, and approach the exercise with an open mind. Take the cord of the pendulum between thumb and finger and set it gently oscillating. Now concentrate on a positive thought — on the word 'Yes'. Tell the pendulum that you want to know how it reacts when giving a positive answer to a question. With me the oscillations increase, but reactions vary with other dowsers. Once you know what the reaction is for you, use the same method to discover how the pendulum gives a negative answer. With me it is normally a change from oscillation to gyration. Once these two reactions are established they can be applied to whatever investigations we choose to undertake.

Note, however, that sometimes the reactions of individual dowsers vary from day to day. It is necessary to re-check constantly. There have been days which, for me, gyrations of the pendulum have indicated a positive answer, oscillations a negative one, which is the reverse of normal. I do not know why that should be so, but if I had not checked at the beginning of the exercise I would have obtained a series of false readings.

Let us return to our original quest for water. We are going to try to locate it by means of a map, which will in all probability be divided into squares. Hold the pendulum in one hand and with the pointer in the other run its tip down the side of the map. Concentrate on the water you hope to find. At each grid pause to ask the question, 'Is it in this square?' The pendulum will give a positive or negative response. Repeat the exercise along the top or bottom margin of the map. Your pendulum will now have indicated a square where the two grids cross. Divide that square into a smaller grid, and repeat the operation. According to the scale of your map, you should be able to pinpoint the object of your search.

An alternative method is to start at any convenient point on the map, trace a line with the pointer in any direction and ask the pendulum, 'Is it on this line?' As you slowly move the pointer to a series of points around the centre you have chosen you will (if whatever you are seeking is to be found in the area) sooner or later obtain a positive response. Now choose another centre and repeat the experiment. Where the lines indicated by two positive replies intersect you will find your goal.

Because of the difficulties of dowsing on the spot in remote areas of the world, map-dowsing is widely employed for preliminary surveys. The dowser then has some indication of where to begin his search on the ground, without having to start from scratch. The technique can, of course, be used for locating virtually anything, from lodes of tin ore to missing persons. Examples of some of the work now being undertaken by map-dowsing are given in Chapter 14.

The earlier chapters of this book are confined to what may be termed the more pedestrian aspects of dowsing, those which could be accounted for by a theory of radioactive or electromagnetic emissions which the dowser is able to receive. As already stated, no such explanation will suffice for map-dowsing, which seems to take us into the realm of purely mental activity. There are, however, certain aspects of field-dowsing which fit into that same category.

The story of the celebrated tracking feat performed by Jacques Aymar in the seventeenth century will serve as an example. In 1692 Aymar, a French peasant with a reputation as a dowser, was called to assist in tracing the murderers of a rich wine-merchant and his wife of Lyons. Armed with a forked twig and some of the murdered couple's clothes as a sample, he followed the track taken by the murderers through the streets of the city and across a bridge over the river Rhine. At a cottage on the other side of the river, Aymar declared that the murderers had stopped to drink wine. He said that there were three of them. Two small children living nearby confirmed that three strange men had indeed called in for a glass of wine on the day in question. For three days Aymar followed the trail downstream until eventually he arrived at the little town of Beaucaire, where his rod led him to the gates of the prison. The prison warder obligingly arranged an identity parade of thirteen prisoners arrested during the past few days. Aymar's rod picked out a man who had been in prison for only an hour or two, for some minor crime. 'This man was involved,' declared Aymar, 'though he was not the prime murderer.'

The prisoner naturally denied any knowledge of the crime, but when taken back to Lyons and made to retrace his steps through the city to the cellar, being confronted en route by various people who had seen him on the day of the murders and who recognised him, he eventually broke down and confessed. He claimed, though, that he had not committed the murders himself but had been hired by a couple of rogues to help carry the loot from the murdered merchant's house. By this time the authorities were so impressed that they despatched Aymar with a troop of soldiers to take up the trail again. This time it took them to Toulon, where they were just too late to apprehend the real murderers, who had left by boat on the previous evening. So the chase had to end there, though the man who was caught was duly condemned to death.

Here we have an instance, by no means unique, of dowsing by a technique which seems to combine the radiation theory with the one based on mental activity. When Aymar stopped at the cottage where the criminals had taken a drink he obtained strong reactions from the three chairs on which they had sat, from the table around which they had gathered and from the empty wine bottle which they had thrown away. No doubt it was from this evidence that Aymar deduced there were three men involved. That part of the evidence is in line with the description in Chapter 8 of the persistence of traces of objects some time after the objects themselves have been removed, and of traces on objects of the human beings who have handled them.

While the reaction obtained from the chairs, table and wine bottle could thus be explained, the fact that Aymar was able to follow the trail, days afterwards, through crowded streets, over flowing water and later on horseback does not admit of any facile explanation. The method employed must have been similar to that of the map-dowser when he points his marker in a certain direction and asks the pendulum, 'Is what I seek along this line?' One can visualise Aymar casting about with his forked twig, pointing this way and that until he obtained some guidance.

This concept comes very near to that discussed in Chapter 6.

There we noted that an affinity existed between insects and their food plants. The fact that comparatively rare insects can find equally rare food plants over considerable distances could indicate that each plant emits some kind of wave, force, current or beam and that the insects concerned are programmed to lock on to that beam. They might have to cast around for a time until they found the beam but once they had done so they had only to keep going and they would arrive automatically at the right destination. It was further suggested that a similar theory could account for the remarkable feats of navigation demonstrated by bird migration. There, however, we would need to postulate that the ray, beam or whatever it was was being emitted by a place rather than a plant.

The theory is reinforced by the fact that not only do migrating birds arrive back at their nesting site after a journey of perhaps 10,000 miles but they stop at the same resting-places en route. For instance, every autumn a party of migrating blackcaps (small warblers) pause for two or three weeks in a clump of berry-laden elder bushes near my home. Other elder bushes in the vicinity, though also bearing a prolific crop of berries, fail to attract them. Probably generations of blackcaps have rested at the same spot in the same season. Not only the destinations at the ends of their range but also the route between the two are programmed into their brains before birth and so are part of their heredity.

Indeed, nothing else could account for the behaviour of birds such as the European cuckoo, which is parasitic on other birds. Adult cuckoos, having abrogated all responsibility for their offspring, leave England for their winter quarters in Africa as much as six weeks or two months before the fledglings, raised by foster-parents, are ready to fly. The young birds thus have no seniors to guide them on their long journey south.

In the case of Jacques Aymar, it appears that he was able to lock on to an emission from neither a place nor a stationary plant but a moving person (or, in that instance, three moving persons). Once he had done so he did not falter.

Let us turn for a moment to another method of water divining. We are standing on the edge of a large field in which we hope to locate water. It stretches to the horizon, and exploring it thoroughly is obviously going to take a long time.

So between thumb and finger of our right hand we hold a short pendulum and we then extend our left arm to its full length, fingers closed and thumb uppermost, so that it acts as a pointer. We turn very slowly in a half-circle, keeping the arm extended and stiff. If underground water is present, when our left hand is pointing in its direction the pendulum will start to gyrate. We now move to another point along the field edge and repeat the performance. This gives us two lines, and where they intersect water will be found. (The forked twig can also be used for this purpose, but W. H. Trinder advises that it should be held vertical instead of horizontal. When we are facing in the right direction the pointer will spring back against our chest.)

Is, then, subterranean water emitting some other kind of beam or ray than the one which dowsers can detect by walking over it? It seems so. The evidence of the feats performed by insects, birds and other creatures suggests that such beams have infinite length. A swallow in South Africa can apparently lock on to a beam emitted by its nesting-place in England and be safely guided on its 5,000 mile journey.

Supposing a dowser, instead of standing on the edge of a field in England, visualises himself standing on the edge of a veldt in South Africa. If our reasoning so far is correct, it should be theoretically possible for him to detect the presence of water (and of other substances) in the landscape before him, even though it is 5,000 miles away. But how does one concentrate the mind and translate this ability into meaningful information?

For our convenience we have invented maps. A map is a device for giving us coded information about a distant place which perhaps we have never seen. Through our sense of sight a map can convey to our brains a wealth of details about the place. It seems that another batch of information may be available to a dowser through his sixth sense.

Humans appear to have greater powers of choice than other species. Most creatures react automatically to various stimuli, and so do we to a large extent, but we have a greater capacity for making a reasoned selection. We can compel ourselves to take a course of action which our instincts reject, for instance, as every soldier knows.

Thus we are not automatically locked on a predestined beam or wavelength, as the swallow is when it starts its migratory journey. We can choose which beam we will latch on to. Jacques Aymar was able to choose the beam he would follow, out of the multitudinous alternatives all around him. Can the fact that I was able to locate water in Portugal, a country I had then never visited, be accounted for in the same way?

The theory is at least tenable. There is, however, another possible explanation, simpler yet more profound, which will be discussed in the last chapter.

13

The Road So Far

The fact that dowsing is not often mentioned in ancient literature is no evidence that it was not practised. Much of the knowledge of the ancients was esoteric, the jealously preserved secrets of a privileged caste. And of such records that were made, only a scant residue have survived. There is no documentary evidence of a knowledge of electricity among the Babylonians, yet an artefact retrieved by archaeologists seems to be the remains of a primitive battery. There is no reference in the literature of ancient Greece to the highly complex calculator or astronomical clock dredged up from the sea off the island of Antikythera and proved to date from the first century BC. The Phoenicians certainly did not write down accounts of their voyages to north-west Europe, southern Africa and possibly North America. It is quite likely that dowsing was the prerogative of a priestly hierarchy, especially as it could be used for predicting the future.

Nevertheless early references to divining rods do exist. Herodotus in the fifth century BC describes the use of willow rods for divining by the Scythians, who lived in southern Russia. In Palestine in the eighth century BC the prophet Hosea rebuked the Israelites for consulting a piece of wood and taking advice from their wands. An ancient tradition has it that when the Queen of Sheba visited Solomon she included among her retainers experts who with the aid of a divining rod could dowse for water and gold. In Chinese literature statements seem to refer to dowsing as early as 2200 BC. A figure in rock paintings of the Tassili Plateau, in the central Sahara, from about 3000 BC, could be a dowser at work with his rod.

From early times dowsing has been associated in people's minds with other forms of divination. Reference in a rhyming dictionary to words ending in 'mancy' reveals a surprising number. The dictionary I am consulting gives 38. Among the better-known are *cartomancy* ('divination by cards'), *cheiromancy* ('palmistry'), *onychomancy* ('divination by finger nails') and *bibliomancy* ('divination by random passages in books'). Divination by a dowsing rod or wand is *rhabdomancy*. All these forms of divination except the use of the divining rod, have been employed primarily if not exclusively in attempts to foretell the future. Divining rods too had this as a secondary function. It is therefore not surprising that the medieval church frowned upon dowsing as a form of witchcraft. The clerics had some justification for their views, though not perhaps in the way they thought, as the discussion in our final chapter suggests. Even today some devout and ill-informed Christians tend to regard dowsing as trespassing on forbidden territory, while in America equally superstitious and ill-informed scientists refer to dowsers as 'water witches'.

Dowsing as a practical art, of immense value to miners, emerges into recorded history in the sixteenth century with the publication of Georgius Agricola's great volume *De Re Metallica*, previously mentioned. So highly was this textbook prized that copies were chained in German churches in mining districts, as Bibles were, and read to illiterate miners by priests. As described earlier, Agricola was thoroughly conversant with the use of the divining rod in locating new lodes and gives details of the procedure. For the sake of his own safety in that bigoted age, he adds that 'a miner, since he ought to be a good and serious man, should not make use of the enchanted twig', just as in our own day scientists convinced of the efficacy of the divining rod have hesitated to declare their conviction for fear of ridicule and downright hostility from their contemporaries. The Reformation did nothing to resolve the controversy, for the Reformers were divided about it. While Martin Luther condemned dowsing as the work of the devil, his colleague Melanchthon gave it qualified commendation.

Queen Elizabeth I of England, realising that her country was lagging behind its continental neighbours in the mapping and exploitation of its mineral resources, made efforts to tempt German mining experts to emigrate to England. Her policy bore fruit chiefly in the reign of her successor James I, when large numbers of German miners settled in England and became involved in the development of mines in Somerset, Devon, Cumbria and other counties. It is said that, certainly for the locating of calamine (zinc ore) lodes in Somerset, the miners had 'great faith in the virtues of the divining rod'. One of the first investigations undertaken in the 1660s by the newly formed Royal Society of London for Improving Natural Knowledge (now more generally known as The Royal Society), under the auspices of King Charles II, was into 'everything related to the Baguette Divinatoire for the finding of minerals'. Results, unfortunately, seem to have been minimal.

Meantime European scientists had begun to grapple with the theoretical basis of dowsing. Foremost in the seventeenth-century investigations into the art were the Jesuits, Father Bernard Caesius and Father Athanasius Kircher. Both came to the correct conclusion that dowsing phenomena were genuinely produced by involuntary muscular action by the dowser. They were unable, however, to explain what caused the involuntary muscular action.

The same century saw the perpetration of one of the most glaring examples of injustice that dowsers have had to endure. In 1626 the Baron and Baroness de Beausoleil, in Brabant, were invited by the French controller of mines to undertake a survey of the mineral resources of France, where they had already done some successful dowsing work. They arrived with a high reputation earned in a dozen other countries and with a small army of workers brought from Germany and Hungary. Starting in Languedoc and Provence they devoted nine years or so to their exploration, operating at their own expense. Though officially approved and receiving official thanks for their services, they encountered some veiled opposition, and when in Brittany they were robbed of an enormous sum in precious stones and equipment they were not compensated, nor were the officials responsible brought to justice. Eventually, having worked for so long without payment, the Baroness wrote a long report to Cardinal Richelieu, setting out in detail what she and her husband had done and presenting what was in fact a comprehensive assessment of the mineral wealth beneath French soil. Expecting at least some recompense for the huge costs they had incurred, the de Beausoleils were dismayed at being arrested and incarcerated, one in the Bastille, the other in another prison. There they remained, parted from each other, until they died. It seems that Richelieu objected not to the discovery of the sub-terranean treasure but to the methods used, for the Baron and Baroness made no secret of their employment of dowsing rods of various types.

A few decades later there occurred the remarkable exploits of Jaques Aymar, recounted in Chapter 12. His successful tracking of a murderer was followed by a furious controversy on the nature of his strange power. Aymar was called upon to demonstrate it before a distinguished tribunal at Lyons in September 1692, and again in Paris in the following year. The Press (already flourishing at that date!) had a field day, quoting one scientist against another as more and more fantastic theories were formulated. One exercise in which the amiable and unsuspecting Aymar was persuaded to engage would have done justice to modern investigative journalism at its most ingenious. He was invited to walk with his rod through the streets of certain towns and villages and discover whether the ladies of the houses he passed had 'soiled their honour'. The naïve man obliged. The resultant uproar, with charges and counter-charges flying, can be imagined.

Aymar's prowess was so well publicised that for some years subsequently France seemed to be filled with would-be dowsers trying to emulate him. Books on the subject of dowsing proliferated and were widely studied. The fact that in 1701 the Inquisition, highly suspicious of the art, placed one of the most popular books, *A Treatise on the Divining Rod and its Utility for the Discovery of Sources of Water, Mineral Ores, etc*, by the Abbé de Vallemont, on the prohibited list did little to deter students and practitioners.

The publicity served to focus some attention on the German miners who, without troubling themselves with theories or explanations, had continued quietly using the divining rod in their work. During the eighteenth century numbers of them consented to having their abilities tested by scientists, who were impressed and puzzled but, lacking a theory to account for the observed phenomena, remained mostly unconvinced.

In the 1780s a young French peasant dowser, Barthelemy Bléton, was subjected to a lengthy series of tests by a Dr Pierre Thouvenel, a distinguished court physician. After Bléton had passed all the tests to his examiner's satisfaction, he and Thouvenel combined to undertake some original research. Among other achievements, they discovered mineral springs at Contréxeville, in the Vosges Mountains, which almost immediately resulted in the creation of a popular spa there. The more impressive their work became the more bitter were the attacks on them. Thouvenel was urgently advised to drop dowsing research if he wished to retain his official position. Typical of the criticisms circulating at that time was that made by a celebrated astronomer, Joseph-Jerome de Lalande, in 1782: 'For so long now, gentlemen, you have been talking about flying ships and turning dowsing rods that one might at last think that you actually believe in all this lunacy or that the scientists who co-operate with your journal can do nothing to dispel such pretensions. It is demonstrated in every way that it is impossible for a man to raise himself from the ground or even to support himself in the air.' It was unfortunate that this distinguished scientist chose to couple dowsing with flying machines, for one year later the Montgolfier brothers successfully launched their first manned balloon.

During the Terror in France Thouvenel and Bléton fled to Italy where, on the death of Bléton, Thouvenel found another French dowser, Pennet, to collaborate with him. Dowsing research and controversy now switched to Italy, where Pennet was subjected to a long series of rigorous tests, some of which verged on the bizarre and ridiculous. As usual, the results were inconclusive. Some of his examiners were convinced by his repeated successes while others, though professing themselves amazed, kept their reservations.

In England the art of dowsing, introduced or revived by German miners in the sixteenth century, continued to be quietly practised by countrymen, particularly in the south-western counties. Its concentration in that area was probably due to the fact that much of England's mineral wealth, which the Germans were introduced to exploit, lay there. As time passed, however, the practical application of dowsing seems to have slipped from the locating of minerals to that of water. Now and again some literary person condescended to take notice of it. In 1840, for instance, de Quincey referred to the Somerset 'jowsers', as he calls them, stating that for twenty miles around Wrington (a Somerset village) 'nobody sinks wells without their advice'.

In this same region towards the end of the nineteenth century two notable dowsers appeared. One was William Scott Lawrence, a much respected stonemason who lived in or near Bristol until his death in 1896. The other was John Mullins, also a mason, of Colerne, Wiltshire, having discovered that he was a particularly sensitive water diviner, he and his sons formed a company which continued long after his death in 1894. Only recently, when engaged in writing this book, I was called upon to investigate the water resources of a big Devonshire estate on another part of which members of the Mullins family had worked many years earlier. 'They used to do the entire job,' the agent remembered, 'finding the water, sinking the bore and laying down the pipes. They guaranteed success. No adequate water supply, no pay. They would accurately predict flow in gallons per hour and depth at which the water would be found.' In fact I understand that while Mullins himself operated on those principles, his sons were not so invariably successful and modified the terms of their contracts accordingly.

The account of how Mullins discovered his ability is interesting. As a young man of twenty-one he was working as a mason on a new house on the Ashwick Estate in Gloucestershire when the owner, Sir John Ould, called in a Cornish dowser to find a convenient source of water. The family came out to watch the performance and, when the dowser professed to find water (his findings being later confirmed), they all wanted to try using the rod. The only one to obtain any reaction was Sir John's daughter, for whom the rod twisted so violently that she dropped it as though she had been stung. Greatly intrigued, Sir John decided to give the dowsing rod a wider test. One after another he called up all the 150 workmen engaged on the building and invited them to try. When it was the turn of John Mullins the twig twisted so violently that it snapped. A well was sunk at that spot and a copious supply of water found.

From this beginning Mullins went on to achieve a tremendous reputation. In more than thirty years of practising he seems to have had an unbroken record of success, for the few failures that have been attributed to him prove, on investigation, to have been the work of his sons; though less outstandingly gifted, they inherited their father's dowsing ability to a considerable extent, however, and had an impressive tally of successes to their credit.

The history of dowsing as traced so far has been concerned exclusively with the use of the divining rod, employed to detect underground water and mineral ores and also to track criminals. But what of that alternative dowsing device, the pendulum?

The only reference I have been able to find of an early use of the pendulum for water divining is a brief note (source not given) in Christopher Bird's book *Divining*, where he mentions 'a 1553 description of a peasant holding a threaded ring over a vessel half full of water and carrying them across country as an alternative to a dowsing rod'. In this instance, the water in the bucket would presumably be acting as a sample.

In 1806 a young German scientist, Johann Wilhelm Ritter, a member of the Bavarian Academy of Sciences and a pioneer of electrochemistry, undertook a journey to Italy to see a gifted dowser, Francesco Campetti, of whose feats he had heard impressive reports. While in Italy he visited in Milan a fellow scientist, Amoretti, who was engaged in a series of experiments into certain phenomena which later became identified with electricity. As an aid to his researches Amoretti was using various types of pendulum, and, assisted by Campetti, Ritter found that he too could obtain unexplained reactions from them. Ritter's reputation being considerable, his work was carefully studied by scientists throughout Europe, who were then engaged in probing the mysteries of magnetism and similar forces. The research which resulted in the discovery and harnessing of electricity was thus closely associated with the investigation of the dowsing pendulum. Subsequently throughout the nineteenth century continued research into dowsing phenomena was linked with that which resulted in the discovery of X-rays in 1895 and radioactivity in 1903. Each of these discoveries were, somewhat optimistically, hailed by contemporary dowsers as explanations of dowsing, and very probably there is a connection between them.

The use of the pendulum has also more occult associations. From early times a pendulum has been employed to predict the future. In the first century AD Marcellinus, a Roman author, described how a pendulum consisting of a ring on a thread was used to obtain information on all manner of subjects. The pendulum gave reactions when certain letters arranged around it were touched, thus spelling out an answer to the question submitted. The similarity to the ouija board much used in séances is obvious. Some such consideration was probably in the minds of those seventeenth- and eighteenth-century clerics who wholeheartedly damned the practice of dowsing. Once admit the authenticity of one particular aspect of this arcane art, and goodness knows where it might lead. Throughout the nineteenth century, too, those scientists who were sufficiently broad-minded to take dowsing seriously grappled with its paradoxes. At the very beginning of the century, Ritter, realising that he could obtain positive and negative responses from the pendulum, wrote: 'Magic was being recreated, and, along with it, that dangerous frontier at which one is capable of deciding questions of good and evil.' Every serious dowser has had to consider the implications of that statement.

It was in France early in the present century that the scientific study of dowsing began to take important steps forward. Just before the first world war Henri Mager, the discoverer of the Mager Rosette (see page 31), gave a series of lectures and published a book, *Water Diviners and their Methods*, which caused a revival of interest in the subject. On Mager's suggestion Armand Vire, a biologist, organised a test of a number of dowsers to see whether they could determine the limits of an immense labyrinth of quarries, some of them dating from Roman times, under Paris. To his astonishment, they did so with remarkable accuracy. Their achievements attracted a great deal of publicity. One of the dowsers who took the test, the Abbé Mermet, also discovered a large cavern, the existence of which had been hitherto unknown. Mermet himself later did much pioneer medical work and indeed claimed to have invented 'the method of pendular diagnosis'.

The twentieth century has seen the formation of a series of national societies of dowsers. Germany was first, with the International Verein der Wünschebrutenforscher in 1920; then France, with its Association des Amis de la Radiesthesie in 1930. The name 'radiesthesie', derived from a Latin root associated with 'radiation' and a Greek word for 'perception', has now been widely adopted and adapted for use in many languages. Its founder, the Abbé Bouly, began his dowsing researches by water divining but went on to do much pioneer work in medical diagnosis. When, in 1950 at the age of 85, he was created a Chevalier de La Legion d'Honneur he accepted the award as a recognition of 'all practitioners in dowsing'.

It was at the suggestion of Bouly that the British Society of Dowsers was founded in 1933. The United States waited until 1960 for the formation of the American Society of Dowsers, which is now going from strength to strength and has members in every State. There is, or was, even a Society of Dowsers in Vietnam, formed during the final phases of the war, very largely to track down refugees who had become separated from their families in the general confusion. The chief organiser was a Vietnamese naval captain, Vo Sum, who had achieved some remarkable successes in locating survivors from a sunken ship after a naval battle.

Today's Situation

The time has come to survey briefly the present state of dowsing. In every country where dowsing is practised rapidly increasing interest is being aroused. Societies are flourishing and new local groups are springing up. While many dowsers are contentedly engaging in the now conventional operations of dowsing for water, minerals and hidden objects, others are boldly pushing the frontiers of knowledge into unexplored territories, as, for instance, of health, archaeology and the paranormal.

The British Society of Dowsers, of which I am a member,

organises well-attended courses, lectures and conferences. A good deal of investigative work in all branches of dowsing is also going on, and the subject is becoming popularised through exposure on television and in the press.

Although their organisation is little more than twenty years old, American dowsers have found enough muscle to challenge their antagonists in the US Geological Survey. Incensed by the issue of a brochure entitled *Water Witching* in which the USGS, a branch of the Department of the Interior, asserted that dowsing was 'wholly discredited', Raymond Willey, secretary of the American Society of Dowsers, launched a counter-attack which resulted in the offending booklet being put into cold storage. At the time of writing the battle is still going on, but the dowsers have scored useful points by revealing that two other branches of the Department — the National Parks Service and the Bureau of Land Management — have made use of the services of dowsers. Lyall Watson, in his book *Supernature*, goes so far as to claim that 'every major water and pipeline company in the United States has a dowser on its payroll'.

Besides accumulating an impressive and steadily growing record of successes in locating subterranean water supplies, American dowsers have scored notable achievements in detection of oil reservoirs. One of the most successful practitioners in this field is Paul Brown, who has been oil-dowsing for a number of major oil companies for some thirty years. He has also discovered uranium deposits and the first lode of platinum-bearing ore ever found in the United States.

During the Vietnam war dowsing was extensively employed by the US Marines for locating tunnels, booby traps and other devices used by the enemy. As a test of what dowsers could do in this connection a training centre in Virginia was constructed and equipped with every type of ambush and booby trap that could be devised the replica of a typical Vietnam village. Louis Matacia, a dowser who had volunteered for the test, located them all within half an hour.

Instructed by Matacia, marines of several divisions went off to Vietnam and were soon using their newly acquired art to locate not only tunnels, mines and booby traps but caches of ammunition and food. So successful were they and so impressive were the reports that high-ranking officers sent home that eventually, in 1968, Matacia and five fellow dowsers were invited to give a demonstration to the US Army's Counter Guerilla Warfare Command. In spite of scoring a 100 per cent success in a very complex and comprehensive investigation, to the complete satisfaction of all the officers who witnessed it, the dowsers were disappointed to have their skills rejected by the Pentagon. The official objection is revealing. It stated that 'the "cause" of an effect is just as important as the results produced . . . The Marine Corps will again become interested in dowsing only when it can be conclusively demonstrated that the average Marine can employ the technique without regard to his personal convictions, confidence level or subconscious development.'

One sees the problem. The authorities want to be able to say to any marine, 'Here, you, dowse'. And it also wants an explanation of the theory of dowsing. Unfortunately, dowsing does not work quite to order. It *is* idiosyncratic. There are some persons who can dowse and others who cannot. The Czecho-Slovak army, it is said, realising this has enrolled a special corps of dowsers.

Whether Soviet Russia has done the same is not known, but dowsing seems to be more widely recognised there and to receive more official backing than in the West. The general approach in Russia seems to be directed at determining not *whether* dowsing works but *how* it works. An enormous amount of research is in progress.

The 'biophysical method', or BPM as it is called, has been used extensively to locate both underground water and mineral ores in Siberia and Central Asia, some of those vast territories being surveyed from the air. Dowsers working in planes travelling at 200km/hr at an altitude of 200m have been able to locate deposits of mineral ore at depths of as much as 1,000m below the soil surface. Much archaeological dowsing has also been undertaken in the Soviet Union.

The military possibilities of dowsing are, of course, awesome. There is no apparent reason why a proficient dowser should not be able to detect any sort of enemy installations anywhere. These could range from secret tunnels, as in Vietnam, to ambushes, caches of arms, concealed gun emplacements and even submarines at sea. Properly developed and directed, dowsing could render obsolete a lot of intricate, sophisticated and very expensive equipment — which fact alone would be sufficient to array an extremely powerful lobby against it.

Ingenious pioneering investigations into the nature of dowsing phenomena are being undertaken in the United States by Dr Zaboj Harvalik, himself a gifted dowser. His current researches stem from the discovery that the human body is extraordinarily sensitive to even weak magnetic fields. Some particularly efficient dowsers can detect a signal of a strength of only half a milliampère.

Unrelated research elsewhere has established that the human brain produces weak magnetic fields. Hearing of this Harvalik decided to find out whether a dowser could detect the presence of an unseen human being through reacting to these magnetic emissions. Erecting an opaque barrier on a lawn, Harvalik, with his ears plugged to exclude any sound, had his assistants approach the screen from the far side. He found that his dowsing rod would react to their approach when they came to within 10ft of the barrier. When he required them to 'think exciting thoughts', such as of sex or winning the pools, he could pick up their magnetic field at nearly 20ft.

This discovery bears some interesting points of similarity with that of Backster, who found his plants reacting to his thoughts (Chapter 9). The plants, however, seem to have been more sensitive than the dowser, for their reaction was virtually immediate, whereas Harvalik picked up the magnetic field induced by the 'exciting thoughts' 5-50sec after they had been formed (see also T. C. Lethbridge's pronouncement on the matter pages 85—7). The powers utilised by dowsers seem also to be possessed by plants.

Harvalik has conducted further experiments to try to discover the seat, in the human body, of this sixth sense of ours. This he has done by shielding each part of the body in turn by non-conducting materials. He has arrived at the tentative conclusion that the sensors are probably located in the adrenal gland near the kidneys and in either the pineal or pituitary gland in the head.

Another expedition beyond the frontiers of existing knowledge is the relationship between dowsing fields and cancer, referred to in Chapter 7. It was as long ago as 1929 that a survey of the small German town of Vilsbiburg revealed that a significant proportion of cancer deaths occurred in houses sited over dowsing zones, presumably underground streams. A follow-up survey of other selected German communities in succeeding years produced similar results. Confirmatory evidence of the relationship between the disease and dowsing zones was also supplied by work in France (in the city of Le Havre) and more recently in Switzerland.

In the 1970s a German engineer, Jacob Stängle, designed an ingenious machine which he called a scintillation counter, to record the radiation or whatever it is to which dowsers are susceptible. By a moving pen it charts the radiation constantly emanating from the depths of the earth, and when the machine, trundled along on wheels, passes over a dowsing zone the graph makes an impressive leap. So now a machine is available to do precisely what water diviners have been able to do for centuries, detect sources of underground water. Out of curiosity, Stängle was invited to the town of Vilsbiburg to check on the medical findings of forty years earlier. The graphs produced by his scintillation counter coincided exactly with the results obtained by the 1929 survey. His apparatus has since been used in other communities.

In California, another inventor, Dr Armin Bickel, has now produced a more compact and sophisticated scintillation counter capable of detecting mineral lodes as well as water veins. It is being extensively employed for surveying difficult terrains from the air, notably in unexploited virgin regions of Africa and South America. Flying over the territories in question, prospectors have located deposits such as gold, oil-bearing strata, copper and diamond pipes.

Even more advanced instruments are being perfected. Incorporating computers, transistors by the hundred, photomultipliers and other electronic devices, they may even help to reconcile orthodox scientists to recognising the claims of dowsers. One is reminded of Harvalik's approach to an audience of scientists when giving a lecture in 1968. As an introduction he announced his discovery of the 'anthropomagnetometer', a device which he described as 'a potential tunnel detection instrument which consists of a mechanical indicator and a highly complex electronic system of networks probably reacting to magnetic anomalies'. It took a little time for his listeners to realise that the 'highly complex electronic system' was the human body, assisted by a 'mechanical indicator', which was a dowsing rod. But the description was incontrovertibly accurate. It is a measure of our current obsession with our own cleverness that so many of us find it easier to accept some new electronic marvel of man's devising than the fact that there are still some things about the natural universe and even our own bodies that we do not know.

14

What Is It?

Abandoning the twentieth century, let us retreat for 10,000 years to, say, the world of 8000 BC. The Ice Ages which have dominated the northern hemisphere for millennia are at last ending. The great glaciers are melting. The released waters are flooding ancient lands. Nomadic hunters are following the receding ice northwards, finding plenty of food in the abundant herds of mammoths, elk, aurochs, bison and other large herbivorous animals which feed on the well-watered grasslands.

For these people life varies little from year to year. In spring the tribes follow the herds northwards, in autumn they retire to the south. So it was in the time of their grandparents. So it has always been.

The senses of these ancestors of ours, sharpened by constant use and uncluttered by the ceaseless battering to which ours are now subjected, are keener than ours. Their eyes are as sharp as the wood-pigeon's; their hearing as acute as the thrush's, listening for worms moving beneath the surface of a lawn; their sense of smell, which in us is an atrophied and neglected vestige, is as sensitive as a fox's. And they have other senses which have now been largely forgotten, to such an extent that by some moderns their very existence is denied.

Precognition or Prediction

One of the commonest examples in nature is the ability of many, perhaps most, creatures to predict the weather. Within the past few decades we have come to rely, to some extent at

127

least, on the television and radio forecasts and on those in the daily papers. Based now on photographs from weather satellites as well as on comprehensive data collected by weather stations, they are reasonably accurate in the short term, though little more than guesswork at long range. Before such aids were available, countrymen were able to predict changes in the weather by observing the behaviour of wild creatures. When swallows flew low over the meadows they forecast rain. When rooks foraged far from their nests they predicted fine weather, but when the birds stayed in the fields near the rookery rain was to be expected.

Most birds and animals do seem to have an inbuilt barometer. I have noticed that our local cats have a good idea as to whether the coming night is going to be fine or wet: on fine nights they like to stay out hunting, but you won't catch them doing so when rain is on the way. Country lore is full of weather predictions that can be made by watching the behaviour of animals. A cat washing itself excessively is a sign of approaching rain. So are ducks fluttering and shaking their wings; pigs carrying straw in their mouths (unless they are sows about to farrow!); peacocks calling; cows snuffling the air or licking their hooves; funnel spiders peeping from their webs. Cows also have a habit of moving to higher ground and lying down when rain is imminent. Possibly they are staking a claim to a dry patch before the rain comes.

On 30 May 1979, a longish drought in southern England broke in a severe thunderstorm, in the course of which 3in of rain fell in a few hours. The flat country where I live was flooded to a depth of several feet. A few days later, when the floods receded, moles were throwing up their runs everywhere in the fields. But where had they been when the rain came? If they had remained in the fields they would have been drowned, so obviously they had taken refuge on higher ground. To do that they would have had to travel considerable distances (for moles, on their short, clumsy legs). If they had not started until the thunderstorm began it would have been too late. The inference is that they sensed the danger in good time and took the necessary action.

I have come across two separate instances of water-birds taking precautions against floods. Here are extracts from a letter telling me about one of them: 'I found a moorhen's nest complete with eggs. It was at the edge of a pool in a small stream and was built so that the eggs were four or five inches above the surface of the water. A few days later I passed that way again and was surprised to see the moorhen adding new material to the nest. Two days later the clouds began to build up, a thunderstorm broke, and many hours of heavy rain followed. Next day I went to see how the moorhen was faring. The level of water in the pool had risen by several inches, but the moorhen was sitting on her nest, safely above it. The extra material she had piled on had been just sufficient to raise the eggs four or five inches above the new level of the water.'

In the Fenland region of eastern England residents say that when floods are coming the household cats go upstairs to sleep on the beds or perch on the tops of high cupboards. The householders, observing this, take flood precautions. As the Fens are fed by rivers rising scores of miles away, floods can occur without any local rainfall, so in this instance the animals are not reacting to signs of imminent local rain, such as might be detected by a fall in barometric pressure.

The belief that animals also have forewarning of other natural events which we term disasters is deep-seated. Whenever an earthquake occurs or a volcano erupts we hear afterwards that for several days prior to the event the local dogs, cats, rats and other creatures seemed unusually restless and apprehensive. Folklore of many countries provides instances of animals apparently having foreknowledge of death. Quite recently I came across an example not far from my home: 'This marmalade cat which lived in the house next door never came into our house, as our own cat would not allow it. Our cat would also chase away any other cats which ventured on our property. On the day the old lady who was living next door died, the marmalade cat came pawing and crying at our front window. So we let it in, and our own cat watched it come in without making any objection. Later in the day the old lady died. The marmalade cat stayed until it died, some years later. Our own cat became quite friendly with it.'

Dogs and horses are said to be aware of approaching death, and the tradition that rats will forsake a ship that is doomed to sink on its next voyage is well known.

Some people (my wife is one) occasionally have premonitions of impending disaster. They do not know the nature of the catastrophe portended, but when it has happened they say, 'Ah, that was what my premonitions were foretelling.' If our species had, in past millennia, allowed our sense of prediction to develop instead of atrophying we might now find new uses for it.

The Sense of Time

I quote another letter, this one from a lady about her eleven-month-old Manchester terrier: 'Almost invariably I take him for a walk at 1.45 pm. We lunch at 12.30, then have a cup of tea and a nap, or else we read. The dog also has a nap in the same room. At exactly 1.40 pm every day he wakes, gives a prodigious yawn, gets off his dog bed and wanders over to me. If I feign sleep by keeping my eyes shut, he wanders back to his bed, finds his squeaky rubber dog and either rolls on it or bites it so that it gives out a continuous squeaking. And that, of course, is that! But how does he know what time it is?'

Probably every dog owner could tell a similar story. Almost all animals have a sense of routine. They do the same things at the same time, and they don't like the sequence to be interrupted. The rule applies to cows coming to the milking parlour to be milked, to birds starting the dawn chorus, to animals in zoos at feeding-time, to donkeys on the sands at seaside resorts. Their inbuilt clocks are accurate to within minutes.

We ourselves possess to some extent this sense of time. Once we have trained ourselves to get up at a certain time in the morning, as a rule we automatically wake at that time. Our stomachs demand food at the time when we have come to expect a meal. Some of us are able to vary the times at will. If I want to get up two hours earlier than usual to catch a train, I tell myself before I go to sleep what time I need to wake, and usually I do so without the aid of an alarm clock.

In this connection an axiom which seems to satisfy antiquarians and archaeologists puzzles me. In many parts of the world megalithic monuments are said to have an astronomical origin. They are orientated to, say, the midsummer solstice or the spring equinox. A calendric significance is claimed for them. The common inference is that prehistoric men needed to make such celestial observations in order to know just when to sow their crops, mate their animals and perform other seasonal tasks on which their livelihood depended. I don't believe it. I am a countryman, and for much of my life I have been a farmer. And I wouldn't need a calendar to tell me when to sow or to reap. I would simply *know*. Those in track with the seasonal routine on the land have an innate sense of time which operates on an annual as well as on a diurnal scale.

The Sense of Direction

This has already been discussed fairly fully in Chapter 6. It leads birds back to their nesting-sites at the end of voyages of thousands of miles, often undertaken at night. It takes North American caribou along migration trails followed by previous generations for many centuries. It guides Californian-born whales across six thousand miles of ocean to the rich feeding-grounds of the Bering Sea. It enables long-tailed cuckoos, flying out north-eastwards from New Zealand, to make safe landfalls on Fiji, Samoa or other pinpoints of islands in the immensity of the Pacific. It carries elvers from their birthplaces in the Sargasso Sea to the river estuaries of north-western Europe. Most forms of life engage in a rhythmic cycle of movement which ebbs and flows like a tide. Individuals of a species obey an urge which takes them to a predetermined destination regardless of distance. Much ingenuity has been expended in trying to discover how migrating birds, insects and mammals navigate, but the probable truth is that they do not consciously navigate at all. They just go.

Among humans primitive people still have a well-developed sense of direction, which in civilised societies is best preserved by countrymen who have had the advantage of being reared in localities devoid of street lamps. I myself have been so privileged and I became so familiar with the countryside within a few miles of my boyhood home that I could find my way about it unerringly on the darkest night. In later life when travelling in the wilder parts of Africa and Central America I found my sense of direction serving me well. In the extensive travels of a lifetime I cannot remember any occasion when I lost that sense of direction so completely that I did not know which way to go to arrive at my destination. It is this neglected sense of direction that the present generation of young people is trying to rediscover through the popular sport of orienteering.

All these senses — those of prediction, of time and of direction — were once the common heritage of Man as well as of other species. Like them, Man took them for granted, as we do our surviving senses (unless we happen to have lost one or another of them). Life for us could be considerably enhanced if we still had them. We can appreciate that beyond the forces at present recognised by orthodox science there exist other forms of radiation, energy or waves which sensitive individuals can detect. Dowsers have been and are in the forefront of research into some of these unexplored territories, and already new electronic devices are being developed to replace or improve on their primitive instruments.

The Sense of Unity

As we have noted, however, none of these arguments helps when we come to investigate the power of the pendulum to locate at long range whatever we are searching for. It seems that the only tenable theory is that the whole of Nature and of the universe should be regarded as one integral whole, and that it holds in store all possible information about itself. And dowsing is a method — imperfect and not properly understood, it is true — by which we can tap that store.

An analogy is provided by the international telephone system. Here I sit in my study in Somerset, a telephone at my elbow. By dialling eleven digits in the right order I can talk with my daughter in California. By replacing the receiver and dialling another eleven digits I find myself speaking to my son on Vancouver Island. I need, however, to know their respective code numbers, and if I make a mistake in dialling I may find myself linked with an unknown person 10,000 miles away from the one with whom I want to talk.

Nor is the idea of a universal store of knowledge beyond our understanding. We have already moved several steps towards it by the construction of vastly complex 'memory banks', and that within less than a century. Dowsers cannot be sure they have mastered the code. Their methods still tend to be hit-and-miss, but their successes are sufficient to demonstrate that they are on to something.

How then does the dowser proceed when trying to tap this universal store of knowledge? He takes a short pendulum in his right hand and holds it, as described earlier, over a flat surface. In his left hand he holds a pointer. First he checks to make sure what reaction he is getting for Yes and No. He sees that it is raining, so he asks the pendulum: 'Is it raining outside?' If the pendulum oscillates, then he has established that for him, today, oscillation indicates 'Yes'. To be absolutely sure, he asks several further questions to which he knows the answers, until the positive and negative reactions of the pendulum are clear beyond doubt.

He next enquires: is it wise (permissible, useful) to undertake the enquiry I have in mind? Shall I obtain valid answers?

There are two very good reasons for this, which are worth amplifying. One is that there are many subjects about which we know so little that it is difficult if not impossible to formulate questions. For instance, suppose that a sixteenth-century astronomer, equipped with a pendulum, had wanted to enquire whether a man would ever stand on the moon. He might, if his technique and skill were equal to it, have obtained a positive answer. But what could he ask next? By a process of elimination he might have discovered in which century and indeed in which year the feat would be accomplished, but that would have been of academic interest only to him. He could not ask 'How?' because the pendulum can answer only Yes or No, and he did not possess enough information to ask intelligent questions about the twentieth-century techniques which made the space-craft voyage to the moon possible. He is at a loss. (One may have a suspicion, however, that Swift's uncanny knowledge about the moons of Mars may have been acquired in this way.)

Again, suppose a present-day archaeologist acquires one of T. C. Lethbridge's sling-stones (see page 85) and by a series of questions elicits the date on which it was last used. He can obtain confirmation that this happened in a battle for which we have some slight documentary evidence. He can discover that the stone was thrown in anger by a man aged twenty-five. But what else? He does not know enough about the period to ask the questions that would give him the information he would like to have. If he wants to know details of the battle and of the events leading up to it and deriving from it, he simply has to guess and then to ask the pendulum whether his guesses are right.

The other impediment is that apparently the pendulum cannot be used for personal gain! There seems to be a blockage. So it is of little use to ask if your selection for the Derby winner is correct!

Once the dowser has determined the reactions of the pendulum and has confirmation that it is 'legitimate' for him to conduct the proposed inquiry, he will find it helpful to write down the questions he wishes to ask. Using the pointer, he points to each question in turn and observes the reaction of the pendulum, swinging over the bare table-top.

'I have lost my silver pen; is it in the house?' Yes.
'Is it in this room?' No.
'Is it in the living room?' No.
'Is it in my bedroom?' Yes.
'Has it rolled under the carpet?' No.
'Is it in the wardrobe?' Yes.

At this point he remembers that he had it when wearing an old sports jacket three days ago. He opens the wardrobe door, examines the sports jacket and finds the pen in its lining.

Despite its limitations it is easy to see how useful this dowsing technique could be to a scientist, a detective, an archaeologist or a doctor. A scientist could ask whether the research on which he is engaged is on the right lines and whether what he proposes to do next is the most productive course available. A detective could eliminate a lot of fruitless inquiries and save himself an immense amount of time and trouble. A doctor would find it a valuable aid to diagnosis. And for the archaeologist it could obviate the necessity for a vast amount of exploratory spade-work as well helping him to avoid unnecessary damage. Map-dowsers use their pendulum for preliminary surveys and then check their findings on the ground. Scientists, detectives, archaeologists and doctors could similarly use the pendulum for preliminary work and then check by the other techniques available to them. They need not rely on it exclusively to begin with. Confidence would come with experience.

Nevertheless, it is not difficult to appreciate why dowsing is so often rejected or regarded with suspicion by those to whom it would be most useful. It may help to enumerate the reasons.

One has been the absence of a satisfactory theory to explain all the observed phenomena. The objection is now being overcome as far as dowsing on the spot is concerned, but long-range dowsing by means of the pendulum still presents mental difficulties. It seems explicable only by the theory outlined above.

Another is that successful dowsing depends on the person engaged in it. It cannot be relied upon to give uniform results to everyone under the same conditions. Human moods, health, thoughts and other complex factors are involved. The conclusion arrived at by the US Marine Corps General (quoted also on page 123), though unfortunate is understandable: 'The Marine Corps will again become interested in dowsing only when it can be conclusively demonstrated that the average Marine can employ the technique without regard to his personal convictions, confidence level or subconscious development.' It seems unlikely that those objections can ever be met — though as already mentioned that does not prevent other armies from using dowsing for military purposes.

A third handicap is posed by the past associations of dowsing with the supernatural. The list of 38 nouns with the suffix 'mancy', meaning 'divination', on page 114 reminds us of the wide range of superstitious practices whereby in times past soothsayers attempted to read omens and tell fortunes: by observing the behaviour of candle-flames, dice, oil poured on water, cocks pecking at grain, warm entrails, molten wax and suchlike oddities. Rhabdomancy, or divination by the dowsing-rod, is included among them. The use of the pendulum is also akin to the use of the ouija board and other devices widely employed in attempts to make contact with the dead. And indeed, one has to admit that it *is* difficult to draw a logical line between such dabbling with the occult and the more mundane uses we have been considering earlier in this chapter.

The final objection is less worthy. Highly qualified professional men tend to see it as a short cut tempting to amateurs. All their scientific and technical qualifications acquired through years of study and experience may, they fear, be set aside by a man with a forked twig and a pendulum. No wonder they are scornful and alarmed. At the highest level they sense a threat to the ethics and standards of their profession. At the lowest, they see the shadow of redundancy.

Against all these objections must be set the undoubted achievements of dowsing. From the first sceptical approaches to the reactions of the divining-rod to the metaphysical concepts we have just been discussing, an unbroken chain of valid experiences exists. We cannot say, 'This we will accept, and this we will not.' Well, we can, but it leads us into worse problems and paradoxes. Few of the orthodox sciences can produce a more impressive array of achievements than this so-called pseudo-science of dowsing.

And dowsing is here to stay. On one level it has become a popular recreation, like Morris dancing or weaving corn-dollies. Groups of dowsers are springing up and becoming organised everywhere. Some engage in it for treasure-hunting, as with metal-detectors (which, of course, work on the same principle as the divining-rod). Some employ it to probe the occult, in sessions in cosy parlours on winter evenings. Some offer their services, which are being increasingly accepted, to archaeologists at 'digs'. A few go ghost-hunting. At a more exalted level, many are engaged in serious research — research which in due course will result in dowsing being accepted as a genuine science.

In the course of its development, dowsing is helping to force science out of its watertight compartments, to seek for a broader understanding of the interlocking facets of knowledge. For its logical basis seems to be that the entire universe — past, present and future — is one entity, of which we are part, and that we can know what we will about any other part of it, if we will take the trouble to find out.

Bibliography

BACKSTER, C. 'Evidence of a Primary Perception in Plant Life',
  International Journal of Parapsychology 10 (1968)
BAGNALL, O. *The Origin and Properties of the Human Aura*
  (1970)
BARRETT, SIR WILLIAM & BESTERMAN, THEODORE *The
  Divining Rod* (1968, first published 1926)
BELL, A. H. (ed) *Practical Dowsing* (a Symposium) (1965)
BESTERMAN, THEODORE *Water Divining* (1938)
BIRD, CHRISTOPHER *Divining* (1979)
BLACK, S. *Mind and Body* (1969)
BOLAND, MAUREEN & BRIDGET *Old Wives' Lore for Gardeners*
  (1976)
BORD, JANET & COLIN *Mysterious Britain* (1972)
CALDER, R. *Man and the Cosmos* (1970)
CASTANEDA, C. *The Teachings of Don Juan* (1968)
CHRISTOPHER, M. *Seers, Psychics and ESP* (1971)
DE FRANCE, HENRY *Elements of Dowsing* (1971, first pub-
  lished 1948)
GRAVES, TOM *Dowsing Techniques and Applications* (1976)
  Needles of Stone (1978)
  (ed) *Dowsing and Archaeology* (1980)
GRAVES, TOM & HOULT, JANET *The Essential T. C. Lethbridge*
  (1980)
HEYWOOD, ROSALIND *The Sixth Sense* (1966)
HITCHING, FRANCIS *Earth Magic* (1976)
  Pendulum: The PSI Connection (1977)
HOLROYD, STUART 'PSI and the Consciousness Explosion'
  Journal of the British Society of Dowsers (1977)

KERVRAN, C. LOUIS *Biological Transmutations* (1972)

LETHBRIDGE, T. C. *Ghosts and Divining Rod* (1963)
ESP: Beyond Time and Distance (1965)
A Step in the Dark (1967)
The Monkey's Tail: A Study in Evolution and Parapsychology (1969)
The Legend of the Sons of God (1972)
The Power of the Pendulum (1976)

MABY, J. CECIL & FRANKLIN, T. BEDFORD *The Physics of the Divining Rod* (1939)

MAGER, HENRI *Water Diviners and their Methods* (1931)

MAURY, MARGUERITE *How to Dowse* (1953)

MERMET, The Abbé *Principles and Practice of Radiasthesia* (1967)

MISHLOVE, GEOFFREY *The Roots of Consciousness* (1975)

MORRISON, TONY *Animal Migration* (1973)

OSTRANDER, S. & SCHROEDER, L. *Psychic Discoveries Behind the Iron Curtain* (1971)

PAUWELS, LOUIS & BERGIER, JACQUES *The Morning of the Magicians* (1963); *Impossible Possibilities* (1974)

PHILBRICK, HELEN & GREGG, RICHARD B. *Companion Plants and How to Use Them* (1967)

PLAYFAIR, GUY LYON *The Indefinite Boundary* (1976)

RAWCLIFFE, D. H. *Occult and Supernatural Phenomena* (1959)

RAWCLIFFE, D. H. & EVANS, CHRISTOPHER *Cults of Unreason* (1974)

RHINE, L. E. *Mind over Matter* (1970)

ROBERTS, KENNETH *The Seventh Sense* (1953)
Water Unlimited (1957)

RUSSELL, E. W. *Design for Destiny* (1971)

SCHWARTZ, STEPHAN A. *The Secret Vaults of Time* (1978)

STEIGER, B. *ESP: Your Sixth Sense* (1966)

TANSLEY, DAVID *Radionics and the Subtle Anatomy of Man* (1972)

TOMPKINS, PETER & BIRD, CHRISTOPHER *The Secret Life of Plants* (1973)

TRINDER, W. H. *Dowsing* (1948)

UNDERWOOD, GUY *The Pattern of the Past* (1969)

WATKINS, ALFRED *The Old Straight Track* (1970, first published 1925)

WATSON, LYALL *Supernature* (1973)

WESTLAKE, AUBREY T. *The Pattern of Health* (1961)
  Life Threatened: Menace and Way Out (1975)

WHITLOCK, RALPH *The Folklore of Devon* (1977)
  A Calendar of Country Customs (1978)
  Thinking About Rural Development (1978)
  In Search of Lost Gods (1979)

WHITMAN, JOHN *The Psychic Power of Plants* (1975)

WILLEY, RAYMOND C. *Modern Dowsing* (1976)

WILSON, COLIN *The Occult* (1971)
  Strange Powers (1975)

WOOD, ERIC S. *Collins' Field Guide to Archaeology in Britain*
  (1963)

Folklore, Myths and Legends of Britain Reader's Digest (1973)

Index

Affinities, 47–52, 54–8, 60, 61, 62, 70, 74, 76, 84, 89, 94, 110
Africa, 40, 111, 113, 125, 131
Agricola, Georgius, 27, 28, 114
Alabaster, 77, 82
Alberta, 105
Allopathy, 69, 70, 71
Aluminium, 29, 36, 39
Animal behaviour, 57–8, 59, 66
Anger, 85, 86, 87
Ants, 54, 67
Aphids, 54
Apple, 10, 51, 52, 67
Aquastats, 95, 96, 97
Archaeology, dowsing and, 28, 37, 78, 80, 94, 99, 113, 121, 133–4
Artemisia, 49, 50
Artesian water, 26
Ash, 51, 52
Ashwick Estate, 118
Asparagus, 49
Auras, 41–3, 71, 74, 86, 91, 94
Avebury, 101
Aymar, Jaques, 108–10, 112, 116

Backster, Cleve, 84, 124, 137
Barley, 45
Beans, 47, 48, 49, 50, 54
Beausoleil, Baron de, 115–16
Beech, 51, 52, 67
Bees, 55, 67
Beetles, 42, 56, 77
Beetroot, 47, 48, 49
Bickel, Dr Armand, 125
Bird, Christopher, 119, 137, 138
Bismarck, 43
Black Boxes, 70

'Black' streams, 65–6, 68, 92
Bléton, Barthelemy, 117
Blind springs, 95–101
Borage, 49
Boron, 45, 46, 68
Bouly, Abbé, 63, 121
Brassicas, 48, 49
Bristol, 118
British Columbia, 105
Brown, Paul, 122
Buttercup, 48, 51

Calcium, 38, 39, 55, 56, 77
California, 125
Camomile, 49
Campetti, 119
Cancer, 65, 66, 67, 125
Carbon, 29, 36, 87
Carrots, 47, 48, 49
Castaneda, Carlos, 41, 137
Cathedrals, 97
Cats, 42, 57, 59, 60, 66, 128, 130
Caterpillars, 55
Celery, 48, 49
Central America, 101, 131
Central Asia, 123
Cerne Abbas Giant, 98, 99
China, 28, 69, 113
Chives, 48
Chrysomela, 56
Churches, 97, 98
Clover, 51
Colours, dowsing by, 31–3, 37, 55
Compatibilities, 48–58, 59, 60, 61, 62, 70, 74
Concrete, 29, 36
Cones, 40, 41, 71, 74, 91, 94

141

Conifers, 51
Copper, 29, 35, 36, 37, 38, 40, 46, 125
Couch-grass, 50
Cows, 42, 52, 128
Cow-dung, 56
Cuckoo, 110, 131
Cucumber, 48, 49
Cup-and-ring markings, 99, 100—1
Czechoslovakia, 105, 123

Dates (Archaeological), 80—1
Death, 85, 86, 87, 130
Depth of water, Determining, 22—5
Deccan Trap, 39
De Re Metallica, 27, 114
Diamonds, 29, 42, 125
Diet, 61, 62
Direction, sense of, 131—2
Diseases, dowsing and, 63, 65, 66,
    67, 69—71, 89
Divining rod, using the, 9—19,
    22—4, 25—6, 89—91
Dogs, 42, 57, 66, 106, 130
'Domes' of water, 26
Dowsers, American Association of,
    121, 122
Dowsers, British Society of, 93, 95,
    121

Elder, 51, 52
Electricity, 36, 38, 87, 92, 93, 100,
    113, 119
Electro-magnetism, 41, 69, 71, 93,
    99, 100, 108
Elizabeth I of England, Queen, 114
Elm, 51, 53, 67
Emotions, 82—8

Femininity, 53, 64, 65, 76, 78, 79, 87
Fennel, 48, 49, 50
Fig tree, 51, 52
Flint implements, 78
Flowers, 48—51, 56—7
Food, 61—3, 66, 70
Foreknowledge, 127—9
Fossils, 78—9, 82, 83
Fourth Dimension, 73—81, 87—8
France, 117, 120, 121, 125

Garlic, 47—8
Geiger counter, 91
Germany, 27, 28, 114, 115, 116, 117,
    121, 125

Ghana, 13, 67
Ghosts, 71, 86
Gladiolus, 48, 50
Glass, 29, 36, 40
Glastonbury Abbey, 98
Gold, 28, 29, 30, 32, 35, 36, 38, 42,
    113, 125
Grass tetany, 56, 62—3

Harvalik, Zapoj, 124
Hawthorn, 51, 52
Hazel, 20, 51, 52
Healing springs and wells, 68—9
Herbs, 48, 49, 50, 62, 70
Hitching, Francis, 99, 101, 137
Holly, 51, 52
Homoeopathy, 69, 70
Horse-radish, 49
Hosea, 113
Hungary, 115
Hypomagnesaemia, 62

Inquisition, The, 116
Insects, dowsing and, 54—8, 67, 110
'Interruptors', 39, 51
Ions, 67, 92
Iron, 28, 29, 30, 36, 37, 39, 40, 46,
    75, 76, 77, 79, 80
Iron pyrites, 38
Italy, 92, 117, 119
Ivy, 51, 52

James I of England, King, 115
Jesuits, 115
Joachimsthal, 27

Kirlian, Semyon and Valentina, 41;
    photography, 41, 91

Lead, 29, 32, 36, 38, 39, 55, 91
Leek, 48, 59
Leguminous, plants, 50, 51
Lemon balm, 49, 55
Lethbridge, T. C., 39, 40, 42, 51, 53,
    55, 56, 57, 65, 71, 76, 77—8, 79,
    80—1, 82, 85, 86, 87, 88, 91, 99,
    105, 124, 133, 138
Lettuce, 48, 49, 55, 59
Lie-detectors, 84
Life, 85, 87
Light, 87
Lightning, 67
Luther, Martin, 114

Lyons, 108, 109, 116

Mager's Rosette, 31—3, 107, 120, 138
Magnesium, 39, 46, 55, 62
Magnetism, 55, 92, 119, 124
Manganese, 46
Manning, A. D. 69, 93
Map dowsing, 103—12, 135
Marcellinus, 120
Marigold, 49, 50
Marrow, 48, 49
Masculinity, 53, 64, 65, 76, 77, 78, 79, 87
Matacia, Louis, 122, 123
Maya Indians, 101
May Day and maypoles, 52
Mazes, 99
Medicines, 60—1, 70
Megaliths, 97—101, 130
Melancthon, 114
Melon, 49
Memory, 85
Mermet, Abbé, 120, 121, 138
Metal ores, 27, 28, 89
Migration, 57, 110, 112, 131
Mines and mining, 37, 114, 116, 117
Mint, 48, 54, 56
Moles, 128
Molybdenum, 46
Monarch butterfly, 57
Mullein, 57
Mullins, John, 118—19

Nasturtium, 49, 50, 54
Negative dowsers, 96
Nettle, 49, 50, 54
Newgrange, 100
Nickel, 35, 36
Nightshade, 50, 61
Nitrogen, 38, 45, 74

Oak, 43, 51, 52, 67
Objects, dowsing for, 34—43, 89
Oil, 105, 122, 125
Onion, 48, 55, 60
Organic matter, 30, 36, 38
Oxygen, 29, 38, 77, 87, 92, 102
Ould, Sir John, 118

Paris, 116, 120
Parsley, 48, 49, 50
Peas, 48, 49

Pebble Mill at One, 9, 19, 21
Pendulum, dowsing with the, 19—21, 25—6, 29—31, 35—42, 51, 55—6, 59—65, 70—2, 74—88, 103—12, 133—6
Pennet, 117
Photographs, dowsing from, 103—12
Pigs, 52, 128
Pine, 49, 51, 53
Plants, 44—53, 56—7, 84, 110
Platinum, 122
Poisons, 59, 60, 61
Polluted water, 33, 69
Portraits, dowsing and, 78, 105
Portugal, 104, 112
Positive dowsers, 96
Potassium, 39, 55, 62
Potato, 48, 49
Prayer, 72
Prediction, 127, 128, 132
Premonitions, 130, 131

Quantity of Water, determining, 22—5
Quartz, 100

Radiation and radioactivity, 69, 71, 91, 93, 94, 101, 108, 120
Radiesthesia, 121
Radionics, 70
Radish, 49
Raspberry, 49
Rhabdomancy, 114, 135
Rhine, River, 108
Richelieu, Cardinal, 115, 116
Riess, Stephan, 102
Ritter, Johann Wilhelm, 119, 120
Rose, 47, 50, 54
Rowan, 51, 52
Russia, 40, 41, 105, 123

Salt, 38, 55, 59
Savory, 48, 49
Scythia, 28, 113
Sea-urchins, fossil, 78—9, 82
Serial numbers, 30, 31, 37, 75, 107
Sexing, dowsing and, 42, 64, 65, 74—80, 86, 105, 124
Shallot, 48
Sheba, Queen of, 113
Siberia, 123
Silicon (Silica), 29, 38, 87
Silver, 27, 28, 29, 30, 32, 35, 36, 37, 55

Skeletons, 77, 80
Sleep, 65, 85, 87
Sling-stones, 85, 86
Slugs, 55, 59
Sodium, 39, 55, 56
Solomon, 113
Somerset, 40, 115, 118
Spas, 68, 117
Spinach, 49
Spirals, 87, 97, 98, 99, 100, 101, 102
Squashes, 48
Stängle, Jacob, 125
Stonehenge, 97, 98, 100, 101
Strawberry, 48, 49, 50
Striped lychnis moth, 57
Sulphur, 29, 38, 77, 87
Sunflower, 49
Supernatural, the, 73
Swallow, 57, 111, 112, 128
Sweetcorn, 48, 49, 50

Tassili Plateau, 113
Telluric zones, 67, 71, 91
Termites, 67
Theories of dowsing, 89—94, 99—
    102, 109—12, 127—36
Thought, 82—8, 105
Thouvenel, Dr. Pierre, 117
Time, 73—81, 87, 88, 130, 131, 132
Tomato, 48, 50

Track-lines, 95—102
Trees, 42, 43, 67
Trinder, W. H., 33, 64, 70, 111, 138
Turnips, 48, 49, 50

Ultra-violet light, 90, 91
Underwood, Guy, 95, 96, 97, 98, 138
United States Geological Survey,
    122
United States Marines, 9, 105, 123,
    135
Uranium, 122

Vegetables, 48, 49, 50, 67
Vietnam, 121, 122, 123
Vilbisburg, 125
Vire, Armand, 120

Water-lines, 96, 97
Water, properties of, 29, 38, 87, 92
Watson, Lyall, 41, 91, 122, 139
White Horse of Uffington, 98, 99
Willey, Raymond, 122, 139
Willow, 51, 52, 67, 113
Witches and witchcraft, 52, 53, 77,
    79, 114

Youth, 86, 87

Zinc, 46, 115